Science Explorations

- **Recycling**
- **Magnets**
- **Spiders**
- **Plants**
- **Seasons**

Author:

Cherril Jones

Illustrator:
Barb Lorseyedi

Editors:
Marsha Kearns
Brenda Calabretta

Editorial Project Manager:
Ina Massler Levin, M.A.

Editor in Chief:
Sharon Coan, M.S. Ed.

Art Director:
Elayne Roberts

Associate Designer:
Denise Bauer

Cover Artist:
Keith Vasconcelles

Product Manager:
Phil Garcia

Imaging:
David Bennett
Ralph Olmedo, Jr.

Publishers:
Rachelle Cracchiolo, M.S. Ed.
Mary Dupuy Smith, M.S. Ed.

Teacher Created Materials

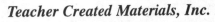

Teacher Created Materials, Inc.
P.O. Box 1040
Huntington Beach, CA   92647
ISBN-1-55734-044-7

©1997 Teacher Created Materials, Inc.   Made in U.S.A.

Table of Contents

Introduction

Science Explorations is a 144-page resource for use with primary students. This book contains five sections that may be used as teaching or supplementary units. Each unit provides fun and exciting opportunities for students to explore science across such curriculum areas as math, art, drama, phonics, music, and social studies. While building a better understanding of science concepts, students will also develop such skills as brainstorming, listening, predicting, inferring, observing, speaking, and illustrating.

Each unit begins with an original poem that introduces students to the basic concepts of the unit and which also becomes a Little Book that students create, read, and take home. The Little Books may be enlarged and made into Big Books for classroom use, or the unit opener poem pages may be enlarged or displayed on an overhead projector and used instead of Big Books.

In addition, each unit includes some or all of the following: games, songs, art projects, phonics activities, bulletin board ideas, sample lesson plans, a culminating activity, a parent letter, and curriculum connection activities that may be chosen to fit the needs of your classroom and your teaching style.

Planting Seeds

My dad and I went shopping
To buy some garden seeds.
There were so many different kinds,
I was surprised, indeed!

We bought seeds for vegetables
And fruit and flower seeds.
We chose a sunny spot to plant
And pulled out all the weeds.

Plants need soil and water,
And lots of sun and air.
And I found out that gardens
Need an awful lot of care!

But soon the magic had begun.
Green plants began to sprout.
The tiny seeds were growing fast,
And stems and leaves came out.

As the plants grew up and up,
Their roots grew down and down,
Helping hold the plants up straight,
And sucking water from the ground.

Then flowers bloomed, and then came fruit—
The part that grows new seeds.
And Dad and I were glad to know
We'd met all our plants' needs!

Plants

Presenting the Lessons

Objectives: Students will learn the ways plants are used, the parts of the plant, how seeds become plants, what seeds and plants need to grow, photosynthesis, what parts of plants are eaten, and the different kinds of leaves.

Unit Poem and Little Book: "Planting Seeds"

Lesson 1

Plants grow all over the Earth. Without plants, there would be no life on Earth. Earth is the only planet that has plants on it. The other planets in our solar system are too close or too far away from the sun for plants to grow. Earth is in just the right place, and Earth is the only planet we know of that has life on it.

Teach students the following action rhyme to "Peas Porridge Hot." Have student partners face each other and hit thighs/hands/partner's hands while repeating the poem:

Some planets are too hot.
(Hit thighs with both hands, clap own hands, partners clap right hands)
Some planets are too cold.
(Hit thighs with both hands, clap own hands, partners clap left hands)
But Earth is in the perfect spot
(Hit thighs with both hands, clap own hands, partners clap right hands, then left hands)
For many plants to grow.
(Hit thighs with both hands, clap own hands, partners clap both hands)

Plants are very important to us in many ways. We depend on plants for their beauty and for many products that we use. But most of all, we need plants for the air that we breathe and the food that we eat. We need plants to live.

Plants such as trees, shrubs, grass, and flowers grow all around us. They make our world beautiful and give us much pleasure. People decorate their homes, yards, clothes, and bodies with plants. People grow vegetable plants such as peas, beans, potatoes, and carrots.
And, they grow fruit plants such as trees and vines that give us apples, peaches, strawberries, grapes, and watermelons.

People also grow grass (cereal) plants such as wheat, corn, and rice. The grass plants are very important to us. People use wheat to make flour. Many foods, like bread, cereal, and cookies are made from flour. Many of our animals only eat grass plants. They graze in the fields and are called grazers.

Presenting the Lessons *(cont.)*

People need plants for thousands of products that we use every day. Trees give us wood to build our houses, furniture, and fires. Trees also give us wood to make pencils and all kinds of paper products, such as writing paper, tissues, and cereal boxes. People wear clothes made from the cotton plant. Sheets, towels, and even cotton balls come from cotton plants. (Pass out cotton balls for students to observe and touch.)

People all over the world have always gathered different kinds of plants and trees and made medicines out of them. Plants were all people had to treat sickness before modern medicines and pills were invented. People in many parts of the world still use these old medicines when they are sick, and many of the modern medicines we use today are made from plants.

Tell students to take a deep breath of air. Ask them if they know where the air comes from. Tell them that plants make the oxygen we breathe every minute of every day and night. People and animals depend entirely on plants to live. Nothing could live on Earth without plants for food and air.

Because plants are so important, people enjoy planting and taking care of flower and vegetable seeds or baby plants in their gardens. Read aloud the poem "Planting Seeds" on page 3. Discuss with students what they learned from the poem.

Review the objectives and tell students they will learn many new and interesting things about plants. Have students assemble and color the Little Books on pages 14–17. Make a Big Book from the Little Book (see suggestions on page 2). Display and read aloud the Big Book as students read along in their Little Books.

Display one or more plants from the following categories (feed stores or nurseries will often lend plants):

Beauty—flowers and house plants

Food—vegetables, grass, fruit trees/vines

Wood—small trees

Clothing—cotton plant

Guide students to observe and discuss the differences and similarities in the different kinds of plants.

Plan a nature walk. Before leaving, label these sections on the chalkboard: Trees, Flowers, Vegetables, and Grasses. Have children estimate how many of each group they will find. Accept all answers. Assign a category of plant to four student secretaries, and give each a clipboard and paper and pencil. Tell them they will make a tally mark (demonstrate on the chalkboard) each time one of the plants in their group is found. Take students on a nature walk around the playground and the neighborhood. Point out the different kinds of plants you see. After the walk, determine which estimate came closest.

Presenting the Lessons *(cont.)*

Tell students they will use some of the plants and products from plants (potatoes, cotton balls, toothpicks, grass, seeds) to create funny decorations for the classroom. Present the Hairy Potato Head activity on page 18.

Reproduce and send home the Parent Letter on page 19.

Curriculum Connections

Phonics: Sing to the tune of "Here We Go 'Round the Mulberry Bush."

> *The sound that we hear in "plants" is "p."*
> *P says "p"; P says "p."*
> *The sound that we hear in "plants" is "p."*
> *So early in the morning.*

Math: Have students measure ingredients in a simple biscuit recipe. (Follow directions on a box of biscuit mix.) Explain that biscuits are made from flour, which comes from the grass plant wheat. After baking the biscuits, allow students to enjoy them with a variety of fruit jams or preserves. Have students sample each one. Make a bar graph showing which fruit jams were the most favorite and which the least favorite.

Lesson 2

Read aloud the Big Book as students read along in their Little Books. Ask students what parts of the plant were mentioned in the poem. Tell students they will learn about the parts of a plant. Use the Flannel Board Patterns on pages 20–22 to explain the parts of a plant as you construct a flower.

Tell students that most plants have four main parts. These parts are necessary for the plant to get bigger and to make new seeds so that more plants like it will be able to grow.

The **root** is the first part of the plant that begins to grow. Most roots grow under the ground. They take in water and minerals from the soil to help the plant grow. Roots also have another important job—they help keep the plant in the ground. Roots grow deep into the earth. A plant has many, many roots. Some are very tiny and as thin as a hair. These tiny root hairs take water up into the plant. The roots of some plants store, or keep, the food the rest of the plant will need to grow. Ask students whether they would like to eat plant roots.

Many times the roots under the ground are as big as the plant on top of the ground. A tree has many very large roots. It could not stand up when the wind blew if it had no roots in the ground. Demonstrate by standing a stick on the top of a cup of soil that it cannot stand by itself. Then show putting the stick deep into the soil until it is able to stand alone.

Presenting the Lessons *(cont.)*

The stem is the part of the plant that holds up the leaves and the flowers so that it can get sunlight. Plants must have sunlight in order to make food. Some stems are very large. The trunk, branches, and twigs of trees are all stems. Some stems are very short, like in cabbage and lettuce. They look like they have no stem at all. The stem has tubes that go up to the top of the plant, much like straws bunched together inside a cylinder. (Show toilet paper tube and straws.) Water from the roots goes up through the stem and into the leaves of the plant. The stem also carries food made in the leaves to all parts of the plant.

A plant's leaves make the food for a plant to live and grow. Inside each leaf is an important green chemical called *chlorophyll*. The chlorophyll helps turn sunlight, water, minerals, and air into food for the plant. The chlorophyll gives the leaves their color.

Plants have flowers, which are also called *blossoms*. Blossoms begin as small buds along the stem. Some plants have just one blossom. Others may have many. Some may grow many small flowers together on a small stem. This is called a *cluster.* Blossoms can be large or small. Generally the biggest parts of a flower are the petals. The petals come in all different sizes and shapes. There can be many petals like chrysanthemums and roses or only three or four like poppies and pansies.

The most important job of flowers is to help the parts of the plant that reproduce, or make new plants. When flowers bloom, it is a sign that plants are ready to make seeds. Flowers produce fruits, and the fruits contain seeds. Seeds have the job of making new plants. Pollen is found in the center of flowers. Pollen is a powdery material that is used to help make new plants. Bees like pollen. They fill little bags on their legs with pollen and then fly back to their hives where they use it to make delicious honey. Every time bees land on the center of a flower, some of the pollen sticks to their tiny feet. As they go from blossom to blossom, they mix the pollen. This is called *pollination.*

When bees mix the pollen in pumpkin plant blossoms, the pumpkin plant begins to grow a tiny green pumpkin under the flower. After a few days the flower drops off, and the little pumpkin gets bigger and bigger until it is orange and ready to pick. This happens in all the fruit and vegetable plants. The bees and flowers are a team that help each other grow food for people and animals to eat.

Demonstrate how bees distribute pollen by pressing your finger in the chalk tray or dusting powder. Have students use their hands to frame their faces like beautiful flowers. Go to each student and put a little of the "pollen" on their noses, the center of their "flower." When your pollen is gone, go back and get some more, just as bees do. Have the students choose what fruit, vegetable, or flower they are and tell the class what they will produce after they are pollinated.

Presenting the Lessons *(cont.)*

Gather a diverse variety of single flowers and cut them into the different parts—root, stem, leaf, and flower. Put them all in a paper bag and have students take turns drawing out a part, telling what it is, and keeping it. After all students have drawn, ask the students who have flowers to come up and compare and contrast the blossoms. Repeat with the other plant parts.

Tell students they will learn more about plant parts in some experiments.

Roots. Stick three toothpicks around the middle of a sweet potato. Put the root end of the potato in a jar. Fill the jar with water. Keep the water at a constant level. In a few days, roots will begin to come out of the eyes of the potato under the water, and leaves will sprout from the eyes above the water.

Stems. Put a rib of celery into each of four jars. Add about an inch of water and a few drops of food coloring to each jar. Stir with the celery. Wait a couple of hours. See and discuss what happens. Discard the celery and water.

Add a few drops of red food coloring to water in one vase and leave water in another vase clear. Place one white carnation in each vase. Observe the flowers over the next few days, and discuss what happens.

Tell students they are going to make sunflowers, using and labeling each of the plant parts they have learned about. Present the Make a Sunflower activity on page 23.

Curriculum Connections

Phonics: Reproduce for each student a Flower Phonics activity sheet on page 24. Have them cut out and color the petals and center of the flower; then glue the petals that have the sound of *p* around the center of the blossom. Direct students to glue the flower to the top of a craft stick. Show them how to hand tear leaves from green construction paper and attach to the stick. Provide brown string or twine to attach as roots.

Math/Color Recognition: Reinforce color recognition, counting, and simple addition, and subtraction by teaching the finger play Counting Plants on page 25. Color appropriately and show the pictures on pages 26–30 as you do the finger play.

Lesson 3

Read aloud the Big Book as students read along in their Little Books. Ask students what happened to the seeds mentioned in the poem. Tell students they will learn some interesting things about the important job that seeds have in making plants. Elicit from students that the seeds of a plant are found in a plant's fruit.

Presenting the Lessons *(cont.)*

Display various seed packets and discuss the pictures on the fronts. Tell students that the plants they see all begin as the seeds inside the packets. Elicit from students that planting carrot seeds makes carrots grow (not corn, etc.). Tell students that a law of nature is that every plant grows from its own seed.

Display a variety of seeds. Explain that seeds come in all sizes, shapes, and colors. Allow students an opportunity to examine the seeds and discuss the similarities and differences among them. Also bring several fruits to cut open and show the seed patterns inside.

Different seeds are scattered in different ways. Some seeds look like little parachutes or propellers. They are scattered by the wind. Other seeds are sticky or have burrs on them that stick on the fur and hair of animals. The animals carry them away. Often birds eat the seeds of plants. They fly away, and their droppings leave the seeds in a new place. Water takes some seeds to other places. Other plants have seed pods that pop open and send the seeds out in a little explosion. Then the wind carries them away.

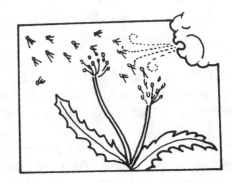

Tell students that when seeds land in a spot and begin to grow, it is called *germination*. Seeds need four things to grow—sunshine, water, air, and soil. Show students a lima bean seed that has been soaked in water overnight and one that has not. Point out the seed coat and the seed leaves. Carefully open the two parts and show students the embryo inside. Tell students that the secret of every seed is that there is a baby plant inside.

Use the How a Seed Grows Into a Plant chart on page 31 and make a poster to explain the seed life cycle from seed to sprout. Tell students they will watch seeds sprout. Explain that seeds can become sprouts without planting them in dirt. They can live without soil for a little while, and that makes it easy to see what happens to a growing seed. Present the Little Sprout experiment on page 32. **Note:** The beans can be planted in dirt and dug up for observation.

Tell students that scientists who study plants are called *botanists*. They have discovered thousands of different kinds of plants, and every year they discover even more. Botanists put together in a group all the plants that reproduce and grow in the same way. *Reproduce* means to make baby plants that look like the parent plant. Sorting plants into different groups, or families, is called *classifying*.

Presenting the Lessons *(cont.)*

Curriculum Connections

Music and Movement: Choose four students to be seeds. Have the rest of the class pair up and stand in a circle. Have each pair hold hands at waist level to form the ground. Sing the following verse to the tune of "Here We Go 'Round the Mulberry Bush," each time substituting different seeds.

> *Here we go 'round the (carrot) seeds,*
> *The (carrot) seeds, the (carrot) seeds.*
> *Here we go 'round the (carrot) seeds,*
> *All day long.*

Have the four "seeds" crawl on the floor under the ground (students' hands). When "All day long" is sung, the seeds grow into plants and stand up. The seeds are caught by pairs and trade places with one of the "ground" students. Continue until all students have a chance to be a seed.

Math: Divide the class into small groups. Give each group a cup of different kinds of large seeds such as red beans, pinto beans (large and small), peas, corn, pumpkin, etc. Ask the groups to sort the beans into quantity cups in sets of 10. Put these cups on a floor graph according to kind. Place any cups with less than 10 last on the graph. Count the number of cups of each kind. Count the number of seeds by tens (10 per cup), and record the number at the top of the graph.

Lesson 4

Read aloud the Big Book as students act out the poem. Have half the class be the child and the other half the dad. Review orally what they did to make their garden grow (sequence—prepare the soil, plant the seed, water the seed). Ask students what kind of spot they would have chosen for their garden (sunny). Teach the following finger play:

I'm a tiny little plant, (*one finger up*)

But I'll grow big and tall. (*hands above head, fingers spread*)

With sunshine, soil, water, and air— (*one finger, two, three, four*)

Four things I need—that's all! (*hands out, palms up*)

Tell students that plants need good soil, sunshine, water, and air to grow strong and healthy. Tell them that even though plants give people and animals food, they have to make their own food to live. Living things change and grow. People, plants, and animals are living things. Other things on Earth are nonliving things; they cannot grow. Rocks, chairs, toys, books, and cars are examples of nonliving things.

In the world of living things there are two main kingdoms—the plant kingdom and the animal kingdom. Ask students, "What kingdom do people belong in?" All animals and plants are alive and need food so they can grow and change. But animals and plants are different in many ways. Remember that all living things need food, water, and air to live. Plants and animals get these necessary things in different ways.

Presenting the Lessons *(cont.)*

Animals cannot make their own food. They must move around to find it. Plants can't move around like animals can, so they have to make their own food. Animals breathe in a part of the air called *oxygen* and breathe out a part of the air called *carbon dioxide*. Plants use carbon dioxide and give back out oxygen. And animals drink water while plants pull it up through their roots.

Display the Photosynthesis diagram on page 33. Tell students that the way plants make their food is called *photosynthesis*. A plant's food is made in its leaves. Sun and carbon dioxide go into the leaves through tiny openings. These little holes also give out oxygen. Remember that leaves have a green chemical called *chlorophyll*. The chlorophyll in the leaves turns sunlight into energy. This energy mixes with carbon dioxide and water to make sugar and starches that are food for the plant. Starches can be stored by the plant and used when the plant needs it. Different plants store food in different parts of the plant.

Tell students they will experiment to discover what happens to plants when they don't get sunshine, soil, water, or air. Present the What Do Plants Need? activity on page 34.

Curriculum Connections

Creative Drama: On four construction paper headbands, draw a picture of one of the essential elements for plants: sun, soil, water, air. Have three students put on the headbands. Have the other students crouch down on the floor, making themselves into little seeds. Have the sun, water, soil and air circulate around the seeds. The seeds will begin to grow until they are standing with arms outstretched. To reinforce the concept of needing all four elements, have the seeds crouch down with eyes closed and have one of the elements hide. Something is missing that the plants need to grow.

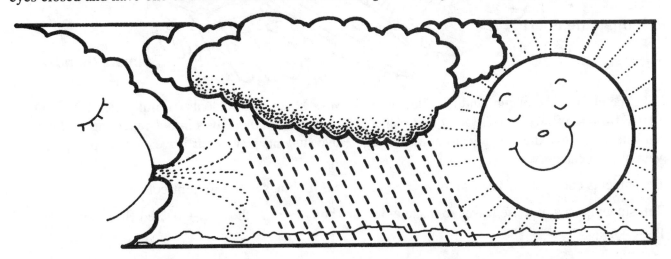

Phonics: Make picture dictionary charts by enlarging the "P" section of a children's picture dictionary. Suggested: *The New Color-Picture Dictionary for Children*, Archie Bennett, Consolidated Book Publishers. Secure the dictionary charts to a flat surface. Blindfold a student and give him or her a sticker to place on the charts. Read the word and give a short definition. Write the word on the chalkboard. Continue until each student has had a turn. Classify the "P" words by heading three columns Animal, Plant, and Nonliving. Classify the words you have written on the board in the correct column. Count the words in each column. Record the number at the bottom of the list. Which column had the most? Which had the fewest?

Presenting the Lessons *(cont.)*

Classifying: Ask a student to tell his or her first and last name or family name. Write this information on the chalkboard. Have the student describe each member of his or her family and draw a stick figure under his or her family name. Count how many family members there are. Repeat with other students. Explain that while we are all people, we can be classified into different families. Explore other ways that people can be classified, e.g., those who do or do not have on jeans, those with or without pockets on their shirts, those who like black licorice and those who do not, etc.

Lesson 5

Gather an assortment of leaves for students to observe with a magnifying glass. Review photosynthesis. Allow students time to look for the tiny leaf openings, called *stomata,* on the undersides of the leaves.

Tell and show students that leaves come in all sizes and shapes, just as seeds do. The flat part of the leaf is called the *blade.* The blade is stretched over a framework of ribs called *veins.* There are three types of vein systems. They are named for the familiar things they look like.

Display the types of vein systems on the chalkboard or a poster. Have students use magnifying glasses to view the vein systems of your leaf collection. Have them classify and sort the leaves into the three groups.

Pinnate (feather)

Parallel (straight lines)

Palmate (hand)

Take the class to the playground to collect more leaves. Make sure students carefully pick ONLY ONE LEAF from the flowers, trees, and other plants they see. Put all the leaves into a paper bag, and have students take turns drawing a leaf out of the bag. Have students place their leaves in the appropriate vein system category.

Let students choose their favorite leaves and make leaf rubbings with different-colored crayons.

Tell students they will use leaves to make a treasure box. Present the Leaf-Covered Box activity on page 35.

Curriculum Connection

Math: Make a bar graph of leaves in the three categories of vein systems.

Lesson 6

Read aloud the Big Book as students read along in their Little Books. Ask students to name the vegetables mentioned in the poem. Tell students that it is very important for them to eat lots of vegetables and fruits every day. They provide vitamins and minerals we need to have healthy bodies.

Presenting the Lessons *(cont.)*

We eat different parts of different plants. Some vegetables we eat are a plant's roots, some are stems, some are leaves, some are flowers, and some are seeds. Display a variety of vegetables for each category: Roots—carrots, beets, turnips, radishes, potatoes; Stems—celery; Leaves—lettuce, spinach, cabbage; Flowers—cauliflower, broccoli; Seeds—peas, beans.

Ask students to name their favorite vegetables. Have the class discuss and determine what part of the plant they are.

Fruits are the parts of some plants that hold the seeds and keep them safe. Display several fruits. Cut them open for students to see the seeds. Have each student name his or her favorite fruit. Allow students to sample the fruits and vegetables.

Reproduce a Recipe Card (page 36) for each student. Tell students to use their favorite fruit or vegetable in a recipe, such as squash casserole, bean soup, cherry-marshmallow salad, etc. Have them write the recipe on their cards, name their dish, and draw a picture of it. Collect the cards and reproduce them to make a class recipe book for each student. Encourage students to take their books home to share with family members the recipes and which part of the plant each vegetable and fruit is.

Discuss vitamins and minerals and the importance of eating a wide variety of fruits and vegetables every day. Have small groups of students make posters titled "You Are What You Eat." Gather poster board, construction paper, drawing paper, crayons or markers, scissors, and glue. Have students make a body using drawings of fruits and vegetables as body parts. Make a sample "body" for students to use, but encourage them to use different fruits and vegetables.

Lesson 7

As a culminating activity, take students for a visit to a local nursery. Prepare a special lunch of soup and salad. Read the book *Stone Soup, An Old Tale* by Marcia Brown, (Scribners, 1975). Be sure you contact the parents who volunteered to help and tell them when they are needed.

Make stone soup using vegetables the children bring to school. Thoroughly scrub a smooth stone and put it into a large pot. Add broth and the vegetables. Add salt and pepper to taste. Broth can be made by boiling Ramen noodle seasoning and not adding the broken noodles until the vegetables are cooked. You may choose to leave out the noodles entirely. (If making stone soup is not possible, students can have a garden party. Set up a buffet of fruits and vegetables and dressings and let students make their own salads.)

Wash and cut up the fruit students bring. Peel it if necessary. Put the prepared fruit in a large bowl and gently fold in whipping cream. Serve with bread and cookies (made from flour/wheat/grass). Decorate the room with the plants, flowers, fruits, and vegetables you have used throughout this unit.

Make a Little Book

Planting Seeds

Name _____

My dad and I went shopping
To buy some garden seeds.
There were so many different kinds,
I was surprised, indeed!

1

Make a Little Book *(cont.)*

We bought seeds for vegetables
And fruit and flower seeds.
We chose a sunny spot to plant
And pulled out all the weeds.

2

Plants need soil and water,
And lots of sun and air.
And I found out that gardens
Need an awful lot of care!

3

Make a Little Book *(cont.)*

But soon the magic had begun.
Green plants began to sprout.
The tiny seeds were growing fast,
And stems and leaves came out.

4

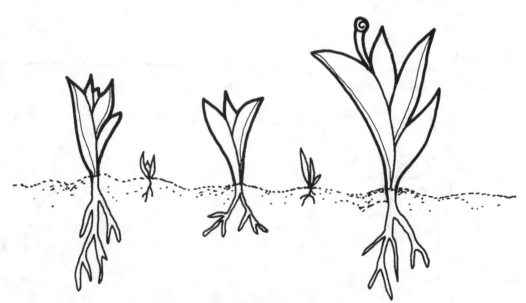

As the plants grew up and up,
Their roots grew down and down,
Helping hold the plants up straight,
And sucking water from the ground.

5

16

Make a Little Book *(cont.)*

Then flowers bloomed, and then came fruit—
The part that grows new seeds.
And Dad and I were glad to know
We'd met all our plants' needs!

6

Here is my picture of a plant sprouting.

7

Hairy Potato Head

Tell students they will watch their potato heads grow wild green hair!

Materials:

- Potato
- Cotton balls
- Rye grass or alfalfa seeds
- Construction paper
- Pins or glue
- Scissors
- Knife
- Toothpicks
- Cup

Directions:

1. Slice the top off a potato and carve out a hole in the potato large enough for the cotton balls.

2. Create facial features out of construction paper and glue or pin them in place on the potato.

3. Fill the hole with cotton balls, moisten them, and sprinkle them with grass seeds.

4. Poke three toothpicks into different sides of the potato and place it in a cup on a windowsill.

5. Keep the cotton moist so the seed hair sprouts and grows.

Parent Letter

Dear Parent,

Our new science theme unit is "Plants." During this unit, we will be learning more about the ways plants are used, the parts of the plant, how seeds become plants, what seeds and plants need to grow, photosynthesis, what parts of plants are eaten, and the different kinds of leaves. Activities will extend across the curriculum to include math, art, physical education, music, and phonics.

As part of this unit, your child will be bringing home a Little Book about plants. Read it aloud with your child, and ask your child to tell you about what he or she thinks about the role of plants in our lives. Encourage your child to "teach" you about plants. To reinforce learning, ask your child what he or she has learned each day.

Our activities may include some of the following:

1. Making a "hairy" potato head
2. Doing an experiment that shows what plants need to grow
3. Learning from a nature walk
4. Learning about the three types of leaf systems
5. Creating a class recipe book

As a culminating activity we will be visiting a nursery and having a lunch party. If you can help with our culminating activities, please complete and return the form below.

Thank you for your support of your child and our class!

Sincerely, _____

- -

Please notify me of the date and time of the visit to the nursery and lunch party. I may be able to help supervise and participate.

Signed: _____

Evening Phone Number: _____

Flannel Board Patterns

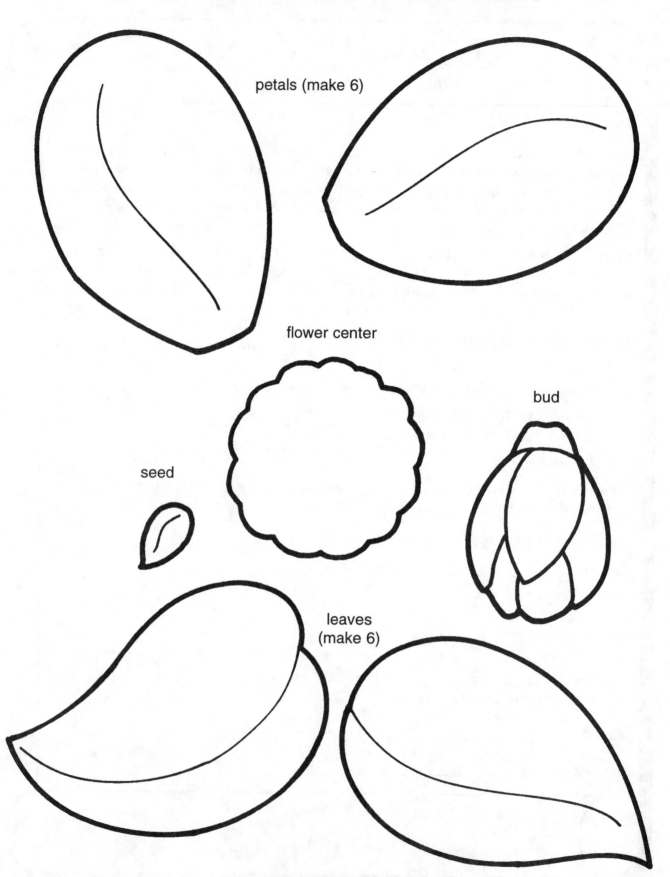

petals (make 6)

flower center

bud

seed

leaves
(make 6)

20

Flannel Board Patterns *(cont.)*

stem

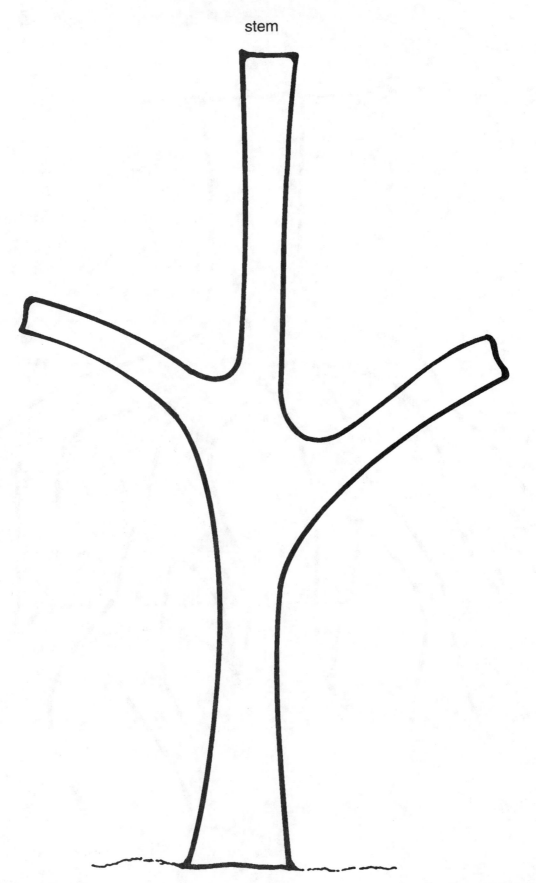

Flannel Board Patterns *(cont.)*

roots

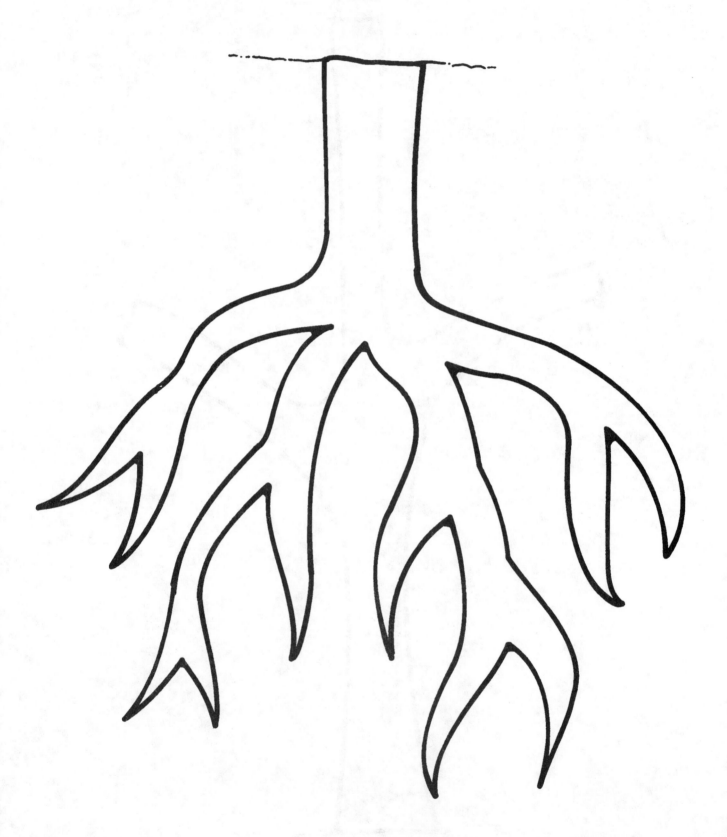

Make a Sunflower

Materials:

- Empty cans, food containers, or cups
- Paper towel tubes
- Small (saucer size) paper plates
- Yellow construction paper strips
  1 ½" x 12" (3.8 cm x 30 cm)
- Sunflower seeds in the shell

- Green construction paper
- Green and brown crayons,
  markers, or paint
- Scissors
- Glue
- Dirt

Directions:

1. Fill containers about ⅓ full with dirt.

2. Color the paper towel tubes green for the stems. Cut one end of the tube all around, making slits about 2" (5 cm) long to form the roots.

3. Label one of the roots and the stem.

4. Plant the roots and the stem in the container of dirt, filling the container completely with dirt to cover the roots and part of the stem.

5. Make the flower by coloring the surface of the paper plate brown.

6. Glue the yellow construction paper strips in loops around the edge of the paper plate. Label the blossom "flower."

7. Glue sunflower seeds in the center of the blossom.

8. Glue or staple the blossom to the stem.

9. Cut out green construction paper leaves, and label one. Glue leaves to the stem.

Flower Phonics

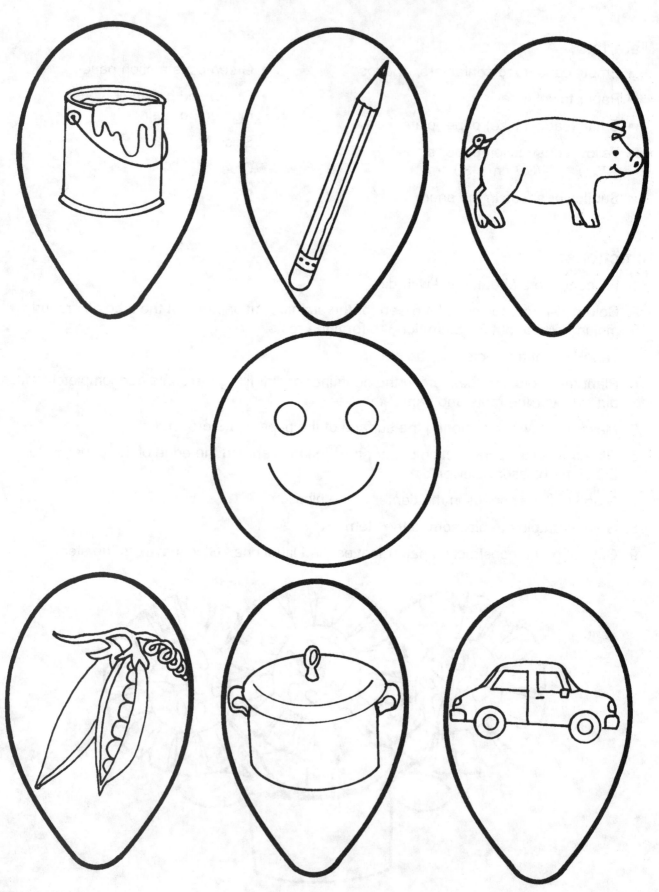

Counting Plants

Sing to the tune of "Skip to My Lou."

(One finger up, arms circle the head; repeat after each phrase)
One black-eyed Susan growing in the sun.
One black-eyed Susan growing in the sun.
One black-eyed Susan growing in the sun.
How many different plants? There is one.

(Chorus—Spoken after each verse)
Teacher: Tell me, tell me, what do you say?
Children: Let's add one more plant today!
(put up another finger)

(Repeat Chorus—Two fingers up, wiggle upward)
Two green pine trees in the morning dew.
Two green pine trees in the morning dew.
Two green pine trees in the morning dew.
How many different plants? There are two.

(Repeat Chorus—Ball hand, then 3 fingers up)
Three brown coconuts high in a tree.
Three brown coconuts high in a tree.
Three brown coconuts high in a tree.
How many different plants? There are three.

(Repeat Chorus—4 fingers up, clap hands on "door")
Four blue violets growing by the door.
Four blue violets growing by the door.
Four blue violets growing by the door.
How many different plants? There are four.

(Repeat Chorus—5 fingers up, they open both hands wide on "surprise")
Five pink tulips—a spring surprise.
Five pink tulips—a spring surprise.
Five pink tulips—a spring surprise.
How many different plants? There are five.

(Repeat Chorus—6 fingers up, frame smiling face)
Six yellow pansies—a happy mix.
Six yellow pansies—a happy mix.
Six yellow pansies—a happy mix.
How many different plants? There are six.

(Repeat Chorus—7 fingers up, walk tip-toe)
Seven orange pumpkins—watch where you're steppin'.
Seven orange pumpkins—watch where you're steppin'.
Seven orange pumpkins—watch where you're steppin'.
How many different plants? There are seven.

(Repeat Chorus—8 fingers up, put hands together and swing)
Eight white roses by the garden gate.
Eight white roses by the garden gate.
Eight white roses by the garden gate.
How many different plants? There are eight.

(Repeat Chorus—9 fingers up, wrap arms together like vine)
Nine purple grapes are growing on a vine.
Nine purple grapes are growing on a vine.
Nine purple grapes are growing on a vine.
How many different plants? There are nine.

(Repeat Chorus—10 fingers up, extend open hand)
Ten red strawberries—share them with a friend.
Ten red strawberries—share them with a friend.
Ten red strawberries—share them with a friend.
How many different plants? There are ten.

Teacher: Tell me, tell me, what do you say?
Children: We have added plants today.

Variation: Repeat in reverse order to show simple subtraction.
Children repeat after teacher: We have taken one plant away!
The last verse would be: We have subtracted plants today!

Counting Plants *(cont.)*

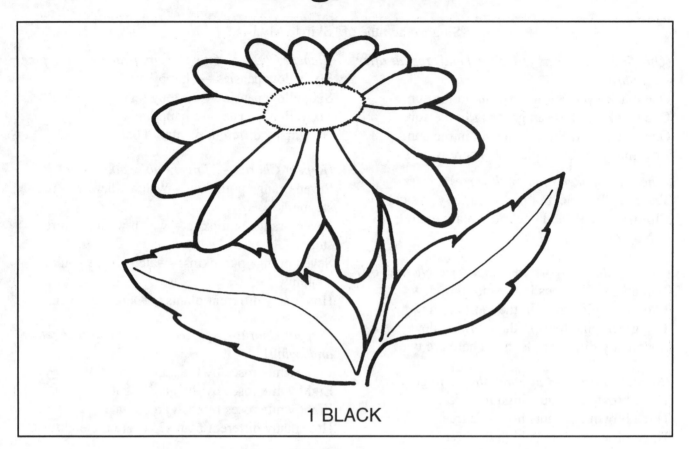

1 BLACK

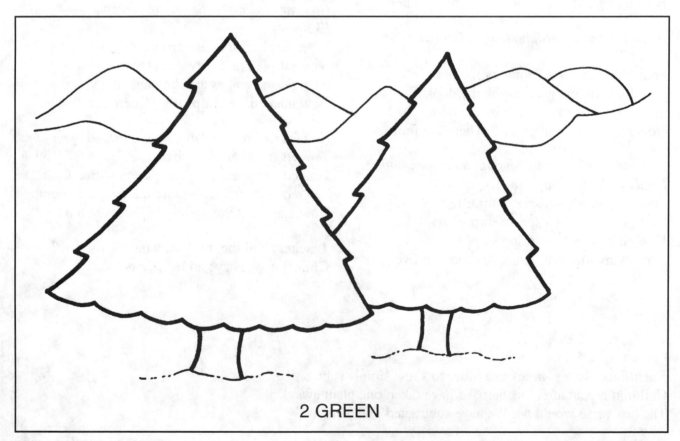

2 GREEN

Counting Plants *(cont.)*

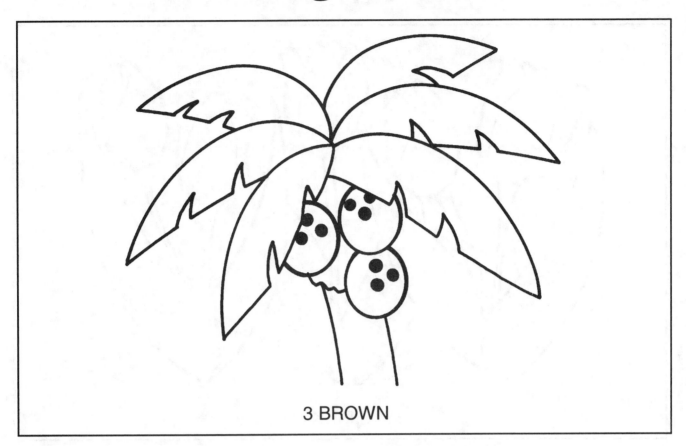

3 BROWN

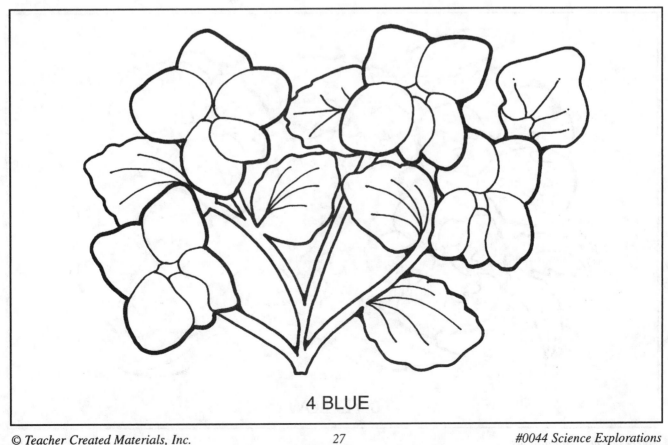

4 BLUE

Counting Plants *(cont.)*

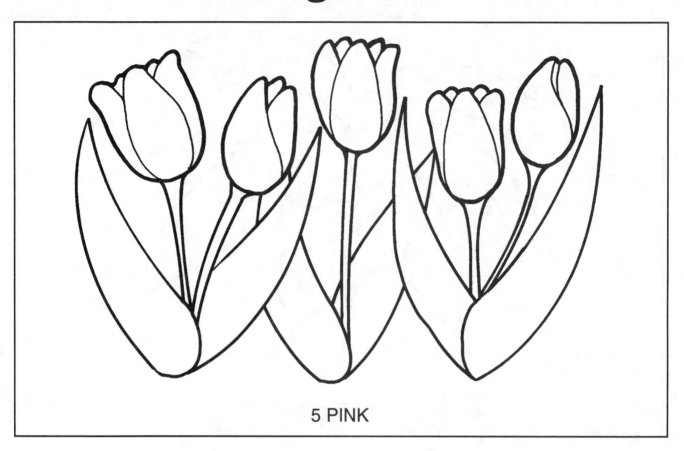

5 PINK

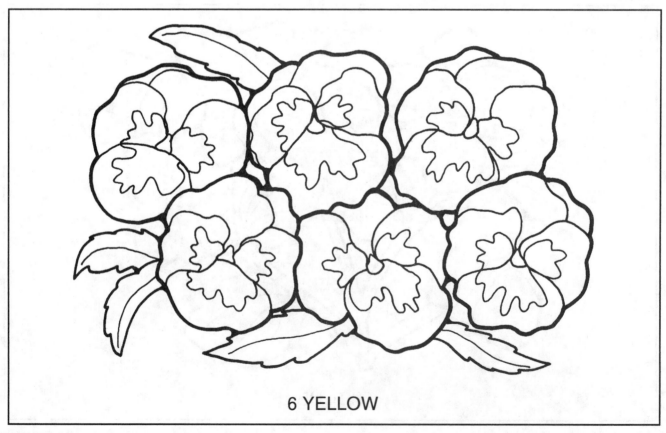

6 YELLOW

Counting Plants *(cont.)*

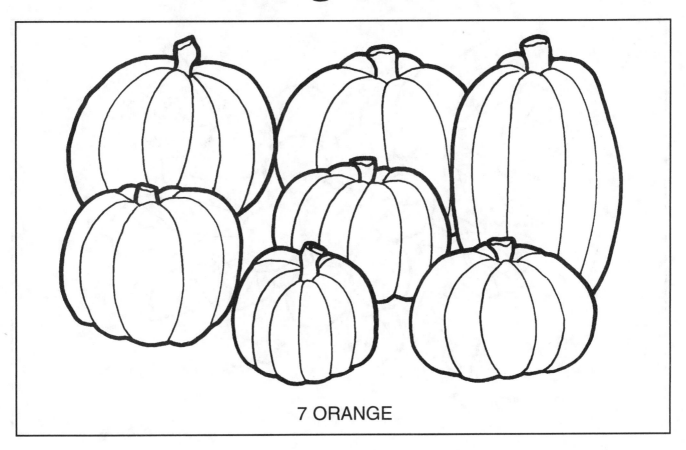

7 ORANGE

8 WHITE

Counting Plants *(cont.)*

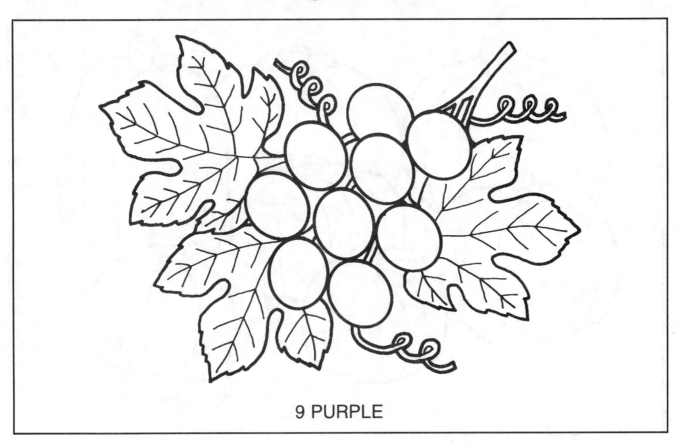

9 PURPLE

10 RED

How a Seed Grows Into a Plant

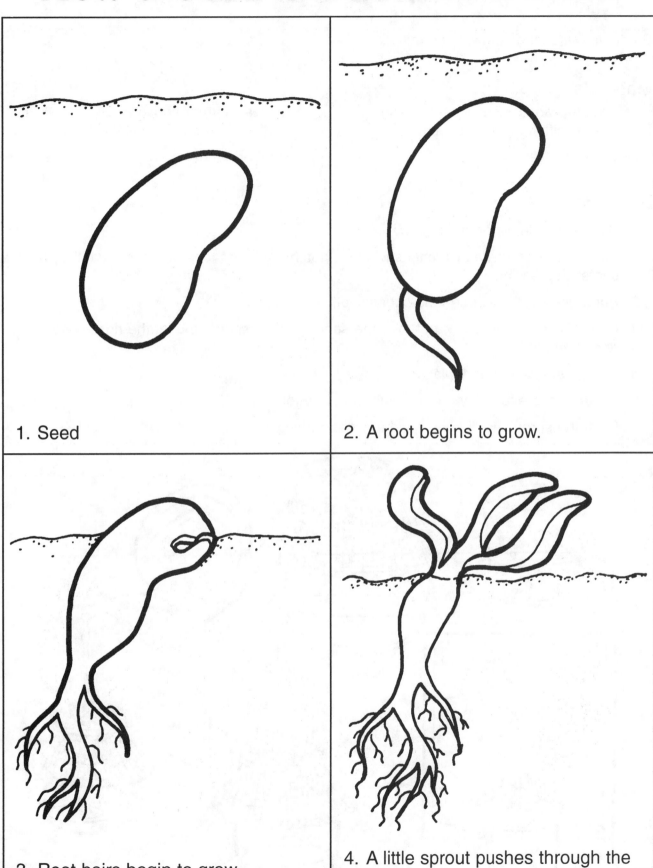

1. Seed

2. A root begins to grow.

3. Root hairs begin to grow.

4. A little sprout pushes through the soil.

Little Sprout

Students will experiment with germinating seeds.

Materials:

- Fast-growing seeds (lima or mung beans, alfalfa, radishes, etc.)
- Baby food jars
- Cheesecloth or fine netting
- Rubber bands

Directions:

1. Soak seeds in water overnight.
2. With rubber bands, attach cheesecloth or netting over the tops of jars so that they have a center depression.
3. Put a few seeds on top of the cheesecloth.
4. Pour a small amount of water over the seeds to rinse them, and let the rinse water remain in the jar.
5. Put the seeds in a dark place.
6. Water seeds every day until sprouts are about one inch (2.54 cm) long.
7. Plant the sprouts in dirt and put them in a sunny place.

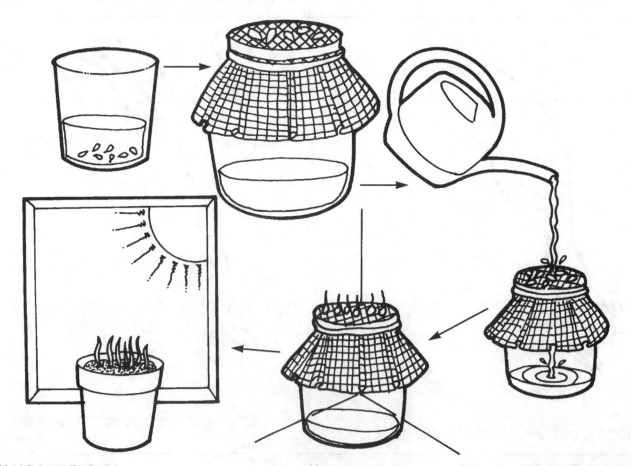

Photosynthesis

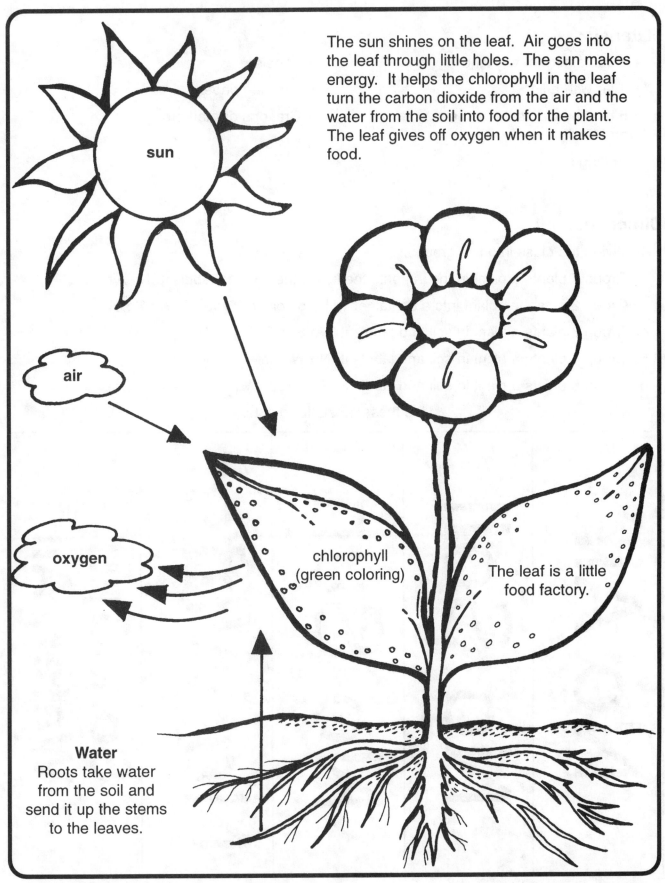

sun

The sun shines on the leaf. Air goes into the leaf through little holes. The sun makes energy. It helps the chlorophyll in the leaf turn the carbon dioxide from the air and the water from the soil into food for the plant. The leaf gives off oxygen when it makes food.

air

oxygen

chlorophyll
(green coloring)

The leaf is a little
food factory.

Water
Roots take water
from the soil and
send it up the stems
to the leaves.

What Do Plants Need?

Materials:

- 4 containers of any kind
- 1 jar with a lid
- 5 healthy plants the same size and kind
- Potting soil
- Labels
- Drawing paper
- Crayons or markers
- Water

Directions:

1. Divide the class into five groups.
2. Group 1 plants a plant in the jar, puts the lid on the jar, and labels it "No Air."
3. Group 2 puts their plant into a container with no soil and labels it "No Soil."
4. Group 3 plants a plant in soil and labels it "No Sun."
5. Group 4 plants a plant in soil and labels it "No Water."
6. Group 5 plants a plant in soil and labels it "Soil, Sun, Water, and Air."

Use these labels for plants.

No Air	No Soil	No Sun	No Water	Soil, Sun, Water, Air

Leaf-Covered Box

Students may use this as a gift box or to hold their treasures.

Materials:

- Shoe box with lid
- Tempera paint
- Assortment of leaves
- Wax paper

- Stacks of books
- Glue
- Water
- Paintbrush

Directions:

1. Place the leaves between two pieces of wax paper and press them under a stack of books for several days to flatten them.

2. Paint the shoe box and the lid and let them dry thoroughly.

3. In a bowl, mix water and glue to the consistency of paint.

4. Place a leaf on the box and brush on glue to attach the leaf.

5. Continue adding leaves until the box and lid are covered.

Plants

Recipe Card

My Recipe

by: _____

Name of Food: _____

What You Need: _____

_____

_____

How to Make It: _____

My Tree Through Four Seasons

There are four seasons in the year
As Earth moves slowly around the
 sun.
Days grow longer then shorter again
And changing seasons always come.

In spring the Earth begins to warm.
My tree sprouts tiny spring-green
 leaves.
Other living things wake up,
The grass and bears and flowers
 and bees.
In summer it is hot, hot, hot!
But my tree provides me shade.
Under big green leaves that block
 the sun,
I sit and drink cold lemonade.

Cool autumn turns my tree's leaves
 colors—
Red and gold and orange and
 brown.
When my tree gets tired at last,
The leaves fall gently to the ground.

My tree just sleeps through
 wintertime,
Bare against the wind and snow.
But when the spring again returns,
It will again begin to grow.

There are four seasons in the year
As Earth moves slowly around the
 sun.
Days grow longer then shorter again
And seasons' changes always come.

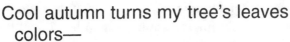

Seasons

Presenting the Lessons

Objectives: Students will learn what causes the seasons, things normally associated with each season, and how weather relates to the changing seasons of the year.

Unit Poem and Little Book: "My Tree Through Four Seasons"

Lesson 1

Read aloud the poem "My Tree Through Four Seasons" on page 37. Gather and display pictures typical of each season. Ask volunteers to identify and name them. Elicit from students the two terms used to describe fall/autumn. Ask if any of them have an idea why autumn is also called fall (the leaves fall from the trees).

Tell students that they are going to learn more about the seasons and why they change. Have students assemble and color the Little Books (pages 52–55). Make a class Big Book from the Little Book (see suggestions on page 2). Display and read aloud the Big Book as students read along in their Little Books.

Changes of temperature and changes in the lengths of days and nights divide the year into seasons. Ask students what the weather is usually like during each of the seasons. Ask whether our days and nights are always the same. Do you get to play outside longer in the summer than in the winter? Why?

Prepare a Four Seasons bulletin board by attaching pictures depicting each season and labeling them Spring, Summer, Autumn, and Winter. Discuss with the class the three months that fit into each season—Spring: March, April, May; Summer: June, July, August; Autumn: September, October, November; and Winter: December, January, February. You may want to start with summer, since most students know they are out of school during the summer months. Label the pictures with the names of the months.

Make four posters labeled by season and display them in the room. Ask each child his or her birthdate and have each tell you in what season he or she was born. Write the child's name and birthdate on the appropriate poster.

Teach the students the song "Four Seasons of the Year" on page 56. You may wish to have the music teacher record the music ahead of time so you can use it in the classroom as you sing. After the first three verses have been sung several times, sing the last verse and call on each student to tell the class his or her favorite season and why. Repeat singing the last verse until each student has had a turn.

Presenting the Lessons *(cont.)*

Curriculum Connections

Math: Show students a large yearly calendar with pictures depicting months of the year. Use the calendar as a tool for introducing or reviewing the parts of a calendar (days, weeks, months) and how to use one. Ask questions such as: On what day of the week does the month begin? How many days are in each month? On what date is the second Monday?

Phonics: Review the **s** sound, as in "seasons." Have students find objects in the classroom that begin with the **s** sound.

Lesson 2

Read aloud the Big Book as students follow along in their Little Books. Ask students what the poem says about why the seasons change (verse 1—the Earth moves around the sun). Show a chart of the *solar* system with the planets and their orbits around the sun. Elicit from students that the word *solar* means *sun*. Tell students that the sun stays in one place while the planets move around it. Tell them this movement is called *revolution* and that the planets of our solar system all revolve around the sun.

Lead the class in the following song:

Twinkle, twinkle, little star.
How I wonder what you are.
Up above the world so high,

Like a diamond in the sky.
Twinkle, twinkle, little star.
How I wonder what you are.

Discuss stars with students: how far away they are, their size, that they are made of burning gas, why they seem to twinkle. Tell students that the burning gas gives off heat and light. Heat and light travel from the stars. We can see the light from some stars, but we cannot feel their heat because they are so far away. Tell students that most stars we can see are far outside our solar system.

Tell students that stars always stay in one place, like the sun does. Then tell students that the sun is also a star. Tell them that unlike with other stars, they should never look directly at the sun. Ask students why they think we can not only see the light but also feel the heat from the star that is our sun. Tell them that the sun is the star that is closest to our planet.

Show the class some models, such as a toy truck, house, horse, and teddy bear. Discuss the things that are the same and different about models and the real things. Display a globe. Tell students that a globe is a model of the planet we live on, Earth. Display a photograph of Earth as seen from space. Elicit from students what things are the same and different about Earth and a globe.

Presenting the Lessons *(cont.)*

Tell students that the Earth moves two ways—around the sun and in its place like a top. Earth moves around the sun in an egg-shaped circle called an orbit. Earth's trip around the sun takes 365 days. That's one year. The sun never moves. It stays still all the time. When Earth moves around the sun, we say it revolves around the sun. To show revolution, place a yellow ball in the middle of a round table and move the globe around the edge of the table in a slightly oval shape. (Cover any ball with yellow paper or fabric.)

As Earth makes its trip around the sun, it does something else—it spins like a top! It takes one day—24 hours—for the Earth to spin all the way around. Spin the globe to show the concept of rotation. When the Earth spins, we say it rotates. The Earth is also always tilted, which means it leans as it spins around the sun. Show the tilt with the globe.

Point out the United States on the globe. Face it toward the sun (ball). Put a flashlight on the sun and shine it on the globe so it hits the United States. Tell students that when the sun shines on the United States, it is day. Wherever the Earth has the sun shining on it, it is day in that spot. As the Earth spins the United States out of the sunlight, night falls there. Then it is day in another spot on Earth and night where we live. When the Earth has rotated one full spin, it has been one full day.

Have four helpers each hold a flashlight shining out from around the sun. Tell students that light comes out from all around the sun all the time. Remind students that the sun never moves. Spin and move the globe, showing how the Earth spins, or rotates, and moves around the sun, or revolves, while always being tilted. While all of this moving, spinning, and tilting of the Earth is happening, the sun's rays shine on different parts of the Earth in different ways—at different angles.

Demonstrate angles using a flashlight. Point a flashlight directly at the chalkboard and make an outline of the light pattern. Tilt the flashlight at an angle and make a second outline. Ask students to determine which beam was spread out and weaker (angled). Tell them sunlight is angled in winter but direct in summer. The movement of the Earth and the tilt of the Earth are what cause the seasons. Again show the United States on the globe receiving direct and indirect rays from the sun by tilting it toward and away from a flashlight beam of the sun (ball).

Tell students they will act out revolution and rotation. Present I Can Revolve and Rotate on page 57.

Presenting the Lessons *(cont.)*

Have students assemble a "My Seasons Photo Album." Help them to staple together two sheets of construction paper for the cover and four sheets of manila paper for the pages. Have them follow your directions: Write the title and their names on the covers. Cut out pictures from magazines and catalogs depicting each season. With crayons or markers, draw a border around the pictures to look like a snapshot. Write a phrase or sentence under each photo. For example, with a picture of a barbecue grill, the caption could be "We cook outside in the summer."

Curriculum Connections

Math: Have students measure their sun shadows. Take students, yardsticks, and pieces of chalk outside in the morning. Pair students to make chalk lines to mark their shadows on a cement surface. Measure each shadow and record the student's name and shadow measurement. Later that day, measure and record again. Read the measurements, and ask student such questions as: What happened? Did the measurement of the shadows change? Why?

Geography: Introduce students to the globe. Explain that the Earth is one of the planets in our solar system. Show them a chart of the solar system. Tell students that the blue parts of the globe are water and that there is a great deal of water on Earth. There is no water on the other planets or the moon. Tell students that the colored parts of the globe show land. The biggest land areas are called *continents*. Show some of the continents as you rotate the globe. Elicit from students that the United States is in North America. Show students that there are other countries in North America—Canada, Mexico and Central America.

Lesson 3

Read aloud the Big Book as students follow along in their Little Books. Ask students what the poem says about summer. Tell them they will learn what happens to people, plants, animals, and the weather in the summer season.

Enlarge the Weather Doll pattern on page 58 and the clothing patterns on pages 59–62. Trace the doll onto poster board and the clothing onto heavy paper. Cut them out. Put yarn hair on the doll. Reproduce a doll and clothing patterns for students, have them color and cut them out, and give them a box or bag to keep them in.

Present the Weather Doll activity. Tell students they will learn about summer weather so they will know how to dress the doll in summer clothes. The clothes we wear depends on the temperature outside and whether it's sunny, rainy, or windy. People have clothes for different seasons of the year. Ask students what kind of weather we have in the summer.

Presenting the Lessons *(cont.)*

Tell students that although the sun is farther away from Earth in summer than in winter, the sun shines directly down on Earth in summer, so it is hotter. Using the globe and a flashlight, show the "sun" shining directly on the place where you live. Tell students that where the sun shines directly, it is summer. Then angle the "sunlight" on the place where you live and tell students that the other seasons of the year are not as hot as summer because the sun shines at an angle. In the summer, the days are longer and the nights are shorter.

Elicit from students what kind of clothes they wear in the summer. Place a square of black cloth and a square of white cloth in a sunny place. After ten or fifteen minutes, have students check the heat of both. Which is warmer? Which is cooler? Why? When summer comes, people put away all their dark, heavy clothes and get out their thin, light-colored clothes. Light-colored clothes keep us cooler because light colors reflect sunlight. This means that when sunlight shines on light-colored clothes, the sunlight bounces back off them. When the sun shines on dark clothes, it gets soaked up. Dark colors absorb sunlight.

Read the poem as if the doll were speaking, and dress the doll in summer clothes. Have students repeat the poem as they dress their dolls.

The weather is hot and sunny today.
So what will I wear out to play?
Sandals and shorts and a shirt are the clothes
I'll need for this hot summer day.

People do many things in the summer that they don't do during the other seasons. Elicit from students things they and their families do in summer: eat and drink cool things, do yard work, go to parks, swim, go on vacation, etc. Brainstorm with students what plants do in summer: grow quickly, get new leaves, produce fruits and vegetables. Ask what animals do in the summer: birds sing, baby birds are born, dogs shed their winter hair, pets need more water, and some bugs bite us (mosquitoes and fleas). Have them sing the following. Sing to the tune of "My Bonnie Lies Over the Ocean."

Oh, summer's the season for growing
Good vegetables, flowers, and fruit.
Oh, summer's the time of hot weather,
But I'm cool in my swimming suit.

Chorus:
Seasons, seasons, there's winter and spring and summer and fall.
Seasons, seasons, there's a favorite season for all!

Talk about summer holidays: Father's Day, summer vacation, Fourth of July, Labor Day. Have students add three summer pictures to their photo albums.

Presenting the Lessons *(cont.)*

Have students begin a "Four Seasons" poster. Reproduce enough trees from the Tree Pattern on page 63 for each student to have four trees. Have each student fold an 18" x 24" (46 cm x 61 cm) piece of blue art paper into fourths and open it up. Tell them to color and glue a tree pattern in the first section and label it "Summer." Have them cut out or tear leaves from green paper and glue them on the tree. Tell them to cut a sun out of yellow paper and put it in the sky above the tree. Have them write their names on the posters. Collect their posters for later use.

Curriculum Connections

Movement: To the tune of "Jingle Bells," have students hold hands and skip around in a circle while singing about summer. Use the words that follow.

Summertime, summertime, a time for lots of fun.
The nights are short, the days are long, with lots and lots of sun.

Math: Ask each student what his or her favorite thing to do in the summer is. List responses on the chalkboard. Make tally marks for duplicates. Then make a bar graph to show the class's choices.

Lesson 4

Read aloud the Big Book as students follow along in their Little Books. Ask students what the poem tells us about autumn. Tell students they will learn what happens to people, plants, animals, and the weather in the autumn season.

Present the weather doll activity. Tell students they will learn how to dress the doll for autumn weather. Things cool off in the autumn because that part of Earth begins to tilt away from the sun. The sunlight becomes more angled and weaker, so it is less hot. Many times there is a chill in the air and the winds are gusty. The days begin to get shorter, and the nights get a little longer. It gets dark earlier.

When autumn comes, people put away their summer clothes and get out their fall clothes. Since the temperatures are cooler, people need warmer clothes. Ask students what they wear in the fall. Read the poem as if the doll were speaking, and dress the doll in autumn clothes. Have students repeat the poem with you as they dress their dolls or sing to the tune of "My Bonnie Lies Over the Ocean."

The weather is cool and windy
So what will I wear out to play?
A jacket and jeans and a shoes are the clothes
I'll wear on this cool autumn day.

Chorus:
Seasons, seasons, there's winter and spring and summer and fall.
Seasons, seasons, there's a favorite season for all!

Brainstorm with students a list of things people do in autumn, such as going back to school, raking fallen leaves, eating and drinking warm things, going to football games, harvesting crops, etc. Talk about what plants do in autumn: leaves turn colors and fall (which is why the other name for autumn is fall), flowers die, acorns and pecans fall off trees, and all plants stop growing. Talk about evergreens— plants that do not drop their leaves and provide food and living places for many small animals such as squirrels and chipmunks.

Presenting the Lessons *(cont.)*

Animals prepare for winter: gather food to eat for when it snows, dig deep holes in the ground where they can make warm nests to stay in during the winter, and grow thicker coats so thick hair can keep them warm. Some animals, such as bears, must eat and eat and grow fat because they sleep all during the winter when the weather is cold. This is called *hibernation.* Many birds and butterflies migrate, or move to another place. They know when it gets too cold, they will not be able to find food, so they fly south to warmer weather. Then, when the seasons change again, they come back. Have students sing the following to the tune of "My Bonnie Lies Over the Ocean."

Oh, autumn's the season for harvest,
Grains, vegetables, nuts from the trees.
Oh, autumn's got cool, windy weather,
But I'm warm in my jacket and jeans.

Chorus:
Seasons, seasons, there's winter and spring and summer and fall.
Seasons, seasons, there's a favorite season for all!

Talk about autumn holidays: Halloween, Thanksgiving. Have students add three autumn pictures to their photo albums. Also have them add another tree to their "Seasons" poster. Give each student a paper cup of multicolored dry cereal to glue onto the tree for the autumn leaves. Have them add the wind in the sky above the tree.

Curriculum Connection

Math: Give each student a cup of shelled nuts. Tell them a number from 0–10, and have them remove that number of nuts from their cups. Tell them to eat ___ nuts (a certain number), then count the ones that are left. Have them add ___ to the ones left. How many do they have now? Eat ___; count. Add ___; count. Repeat several times, then let them eat the rest. (**Note:** Check for allergies to nuts.)

Lesson 5

Read aloud the Big Book as students follow along in their Little Books. Ask students what the poem tells us about winter. Tell students they will learn what happens to people, plants, animals, and the weather in the winter season.

Present the weather doll activity. Tell students they will learn how to dress the doll for winter weather. Winter brings cold weather as that part of Earth tilts very far away from the sun. The sun's rays are very slanted, not direct, and they don't give much heat. Many places have snow, sleet, and ice. Some places have a lot of snow, some places have snow part of the time, and some places don't have any snow. The days are shorter and the nights are longer than at any other time of the year. It gets dark very early.

Presenting the Lessons *(cont.)*

When winter comes, people get out their very heavy, warm clothes. Since the temperature can get very cold, people need warmer clothes. Ask students what they wear in the winter. Ask students whether they would wear dark colors or light colors in winter to help them stay warm. Read the poem as if the doll were speaking, and dress the doll in winter clothes. Have students repeat the poem with you as they dress their dolls.

The weather is cold and snowy
So what will I wear out to play?
A snowsuit and mittens and a hat are the clothes
I'll wear on this cold winter day.

Brainstorm with students a list of things people do in winter, such as have warm foods and drinks, shovel snow, do inside activities, play out in the snow, etc. Talk about what plants do in winter: branches are bare, some plants die, many plants stay alive but do not grow. Talk about deciduous trees—those that drop their leaves in winter but whose roots and branches are still alive, just not growing.

Animals have a hard time in winter: they must use what food they hid in autumn, farm animals need people to feed them the hay and grasses harvested in autumn, forest animals must dig under snow to try to find food. Some animals gather together in old trees, holes, or caves to keep warm. Snakes pile on top of each other in holes to keep warm. Remind students that some animals, such as bears, hibernate. Many animals grow thick, warm coats, and pets need to be brought inside if they live in really cold places. Have students sing this song to the tune of "My Bonnie Lies Over the Ocean."

Oh, winter's the season for resting,
For animals and many plants.
Oh, winter's got cold, snowy weather,
But I'm warm in my thick coat and pants.
Chorus:
Seasons, seasons, there's winter and spring and summer and fall.
Seasons, seasons, there's a favorite season for all!

Talk about winter holidays: Christmas, Hanukkah, Kwanzaa, New Year's Day, Martin Luther King, Jr. Day, Presidents' Day, Valentine's Day. Have students add three winter pictures to their photo albums. Also have them add another tree to their "Seasons" poster. Let them draw snow scenes with chalk. Spray with clear lacquer or hair spray to prevent smearing.

Curriculum Connections

Music/Creative Drama: Sing this song to the tune of "Jingle Bells."

Wintertime, wintertime, the coldest time of year.
When snowflakes fall so quietly, a white world will appear.
Tell students to pretend to wake up and see the ground covered with snow. Tell them to hurry and get dressed and eat a warm breakfast. Elicit what clothes they will put on to keep warm to go outside. Now you will pretend to build a snowman. Teach them the following movement activity.

Presenting the Lessons *(cont.)*

The Snowman

Let's build a snowman
Very, very tall. *(reach very tall)*
A big snowball, a medium one,
And one that's very small. *(measure big, medium, and small with arms/hands)*
Our snowman isn't finished *(wag index finger back and forth)*
Although he's very fat. *(make fat tummy with arms)*
He needs coal eyes, a carrot nose, *(point to eyes, use index finger for nose)*
And on his head, a hat. *(hands make halo above head)*
But look, our snowman's melting, *(make fat tummy with arms, bring in and in)*
Small, small, small. *(grow smaller and smaller until lying on floor)*
The coal, the carrot, and the hat *(point to eyes, use index finger for nose, hands make halo above head)*
Are on the ground—that's all! *(elbows bent, palms up)*

Math: Play a snowman game. Reproduce the Snowman Math patterns on page 64 for students. Have them cut out the pieces and the box showing how to build the snowman. Divide the class into pairs. Each student takes a turn rolling a die and building on to his or her snowman by selecting the piece that corresponds to the dots on the die. The first to build the snowman wins.

Lesson 6

Read aloud the Big Book as students follow along in their Little Books. Ask students what the poem tells us about spring. Tell students they will learn what happens to people, plants, animals, and the weather in the spring season.

Present the weather doll activity. Tell students they will learn how to dress the doll for spring weather. Elicit from students the clothes they wear in the spring. Spring brings warmer weather as that part of Earth begins to tilt back toward the sun. The sun's rays become more direct and give more heat. Spring storms often come up quickly and bring lightning, thunder, and lots of rain. The days begin to get longer and the nights begin to get shorter. It doesn't get dark until later in the day.

In spring, people put away their heavy, dark winter clothes. Since the temperature is warmer, people need cooler clothes. Ask students what they wear in the spring. Ask students whether they would wear dark colors or light colors in spring to help them keep cool. Read the poem as if the doll were speaking, and dress the doll in spring clothes. Have students repeat the poem with you as they dress their dolls.

The weather is warm and rainy
So what will I wear out to play?
A raincoat, T-shirt, and pants are the clothes
I'll wear on this warm spring day.

Presenting the Lessons *(cont.)*

Brainstorm with students a list of things people do in spring, such as play and work outside, plant gardens, do spring cleaning, etc. Talk about what plants do in spring: they begin to grow, first small sprouts, then leaves and blossoms. Animals get more active: animal babies are born, birds and butterflies migrate back there is lots of food, insects are busy. Talk about the importance of bees and pollination (see Plants, page 7). Have students sing this song to the tune of "My Bonnie Lies Over the Ocean."

Oh, spring is the season for growing,
New plants start to sprout in the dirt.
Oh, spring is a time for warm weather,
But I'm cool in my pants and T-shirt.

Chorus:
Seasons, seasons, there's winter and spring and summer and fall.
Seasons, seasons, there's a favorite season for all!

Talk about spring holidays: April Fool's Day, Easter, Memorial Day, Mother's Day, Father's Day, Passover. Have students add three spring pictures to their photo albums. Also have them add the last tree to their "Seasons" poster. Make blossoms by twisting small pieces of pink crepe paper to glue onto the trees, and cut or tear small green leaves and buds. Use the completed posters to display during the culminating activity, the "Seasons" program.

Curriculum Connection

Art: Make murals to use for the culminating activity, the "Seasons" program. Divide the class into four groups and assign each group a season. Give three groups a large piece of white butcher paper and crayons and markers. Give the "winter" group a same-sized piece of blue paper and different-colored chalk, especially white. Have the groups work together to plan and illustrate their seasons. Encourage students to draw large pictures and to fill up the whole paper.

Lesson 7

Prepare for and present a "Seasons" program. Reproduce and send home the Parent Letter on page 65.

- "Seasons" posters and the murals students have created
- Large yellow poster board sun (to be held or worn)
- Globe (to be held) or paper globe costume (to be worn)
- Large cut-out trees with holes for faces to look through
- Large flowers with holes for faces to look through
- Large printed placards labeled Summer, Autumn, Winter, Spring
- Six large question marks
- "Do Not Disturb" sign
- Flags from different countries
- Large individual letters: S P R I N G T I M E
- Display easel
- Spotlights or flashlights

Presenting the Lessons *(cont.)*

Cast

- Sun
- Earth
- Narrators 1–10
- Lighting person—to hold and beam flashlight/spotlight

- Trees and Flowers
- Kids of Summer 1–6
- Kids of Autumn 1–6
- Kids of Winter 1–6
- Kids of Spring 1–10

All: Welcome, welcome, everyone,

To our program here today.

We're glad you've come and we are sure

You'll have a happy stay.

All: Sing "Four Seasons" *(See page 66. Arrange for the music teacher to play the song along with the students, or tape the music for students to sing with.)*

(Position the Sun and Earth students on stage as in the I Can Revolve and Rotate activity in Lesson 2. Position narrators on either side of the demonstration.)

All: Do you know what causes the four seasons of the year?

Sun: I am the sun. I am a star that always shines and always stays in the same place. I shine on the Earth and give it light and heat.

Earth: I am the Earth. This is the United States *(points)*. You may not know it, but I move around a lot! I also always tilt. *(Earth tilts toward or away from sun.)*

Narrator 1: The Earth moves in two ways.

Narrator 2: It rotates, or spins in place, like a top. *(Earth rotates in place.)*

Narrator 3: This gives us our days and nights.

Narrator 4: It takes 24 hours for Earth to spin around once.

Narrator 5: Where the sun shines on Earth, it

is day. *(Darken the stage; shine spotlight on Earth.)*

Narrator 6: Where the sun doesn't shine on Earth, it is night. *(Earth continues to rotate slowly.)*

Narrator 7: Earth also revolves, or moves around the sun. *(Earth begins to revolve along orbit as it rotates slowly.)*

Narrator 8: It takes one year for Earth to make this trip.

Narrator 9: As Earth moves around the sun, the sun shines on it at different angles.

Earth: When the sun shines directly on me in summer, I get very hot! *(Earth stops rotating and revolving to talk; shine spotlight directly on Earth.)*

Sun: My light shines on Earth at an angle in winter. This doesn't give Earth as much heat or light. *(Earth continues to rotate and revolve; shine spotlight at an angle.)*

Narrator 10: The moving of the Earth around the sun and the sun shining at different angles on Earth cause our four seasons of the year. *(Put the "Summer" placard on the easel.)*

Flowers and Trees: We are plants in summer—

We're beautiful and healthy, too,

Presenting the Lessons *(cont.)*

Summer is the time for growing—
Animals, plants, me and you.

All: *(Sing all verses and the chorus to the tune of "My Bonnie Lies Over The Ocean," as was done in the lessons.)*
Oh, summer's the season for growing
Good vegetables, flowers, and fruit.

Oh, summer's the time of hot weather,
But I'm cool in my swimming suit. *(clap, clap)*

Seasons, seasons, there's winter and spring, summer and fall.

Seasons, seasons, there's a favorite season for all! *(clap, clap)*

All: What I Like About Summer

Summer 1: *(with bare feet, wiggle toes)*
I like going barefoot.

Summer 2: *(with fishing pole, holding up gummy worm)*
I like going fishing.

Summer 3: *(wears sunglasses, swimming suit, beach ball)*
I like going to the beach.

Summer 4: *(holds suitcase)*
I like going on vacation.

Summer 5: *(holds up flag)*
I like going to parades.

Summer 6: *(shows new clothes in shopping bag)*
I like going shopping for new school clothes.

(Put the "Autumn" placard on the easel.)

All: In autumn all the animals
Get ready for cold weather.
They eat and eat and get so fat
And birds fly south together.

All: Oh, autumn's the season for harvest,
Grains, vegetables, nuts from the trees.
Oh, autumn's got cool, windy weather,
But I'm warm in my jacket and jeans.
(clap, clap)

Seasons, seasons, there's winter and spring and summer and fall.

Seasons, seasons, there's a favorite season for all! *(clap, clap)*

All: Why I'm Thankful for Autumn

Autumn 1: *(hold basket of food or an original picture)*
I'm thankful for all of the food that is harvested in autumn.

Autumn 2: *(with colored construction paper leaves pinned to clothes)*
I'm thankful for this season of beautiful colors—red, orange, yellow, brown, and gold.

Autumn 3: *(hold up a drawing of your family)*
I'm thankful for my family who loves me and for the fun things we do in autumn.

Autumn 4: *(hold up self portrait dressed in autumn clothes or wearing autumn clothes)*
I'm thankful for warm clothes to wear during chilly autumn days.

Autumn 5: *(hold up globe)*
I'm thankful for this beautiful season and this beautiful world.

Autumn 6: *(hold up picture of favorite autumn holiday)*
I'm thankful for fun holidays in autumn.

Presenting the Lessons *(cont.)*

(Put the "Winter" placard on the easel.)

All: In wintertime, we dress warmly
When going out to play.
"Don't forget your mittens," *(hold up mittens)*
Our mothers always say.

All: Oh, winter's the season for resting,
For animals and many plants.
Oh, winter's got cold, snowy weather,
But I'm warm in my thick coat and pants.
(clap, clap)
Seasons, seasons, there's winter and spring and summer and fall.
Seasons, seasons, there's a favorite season for all! *(clap, clap)*

All: Did You Know This About Winter?
We're going to ask some questions of you.
After we ask them, please say, "They do!"

(This is an audience participation exercise. Stand in front of the audience and make them say along with you, "They do!" It may take some prompting, but before you go on to the second question, make sure the audience and all the students are answering. Prepare Winter 1 to repeat the question until everyone is answering.)

Winter 1: *(holds up large question mark)*
Did you know that some animals grow more hair in winter?

All: *(after each question)* They do!

Winter 2: *(holds up large question mark)*
Did you know that plants stop growing in winter?

All: They do!

Winter 3: *(holds up large question mark)*
Did you know that many birds migrate in winter?

All: They do!

Winter 4: *(holds up large question mark)*
Did you know that frogs dig down in the mud to sleep all winter?

All: They do!

Winter 5: *(holds up large question mark)*
Did you know that snakes gather together to keep warm in the winter?

All: They do!

Winter 6: *(holds up large question mark)*
Did you know the nights get longer in winter?

All: They do: And don't forget the animals
Who sleep all night and day.
If they could talk, "Do Not Disturb" *(hold up sign)*
Is just what they would say!!

(Put the "Spring" placard on the easel.)

All: In spring all things begin to grow—
Animals, plants; you and I.
When we feel the sun's new warmth,
We breathe a happy sigh.

All: Oh, spring is the season for growing,
New plants start to sprout from the dirt.
Oh, spring is a time for warm weather,
But I'm cool in my pants and T-shirt.
(clap, clap)
Seasons, seasons, there's winter and spring and summer and fall.
Seasons, seasons, there's a favorite season for all! *(clap, clap)*

All: Tell Us About Spring *(As each student*

Presenting the Lessons *(cont.)*

speaks, he or she holds up a large letter.)

Spring 1: S is for springtime—it's finally here.

Spring 2: P is for pretty—it's that time of year.

Spring 3: R is for raindrops and rainbows that come.

Spring 4: I is for insects that sing, buzz, or hum.

Spring 5: N is for birds' nests high up in the trees.

Spring 6: G is for gardens and planting our seeds.

Spring 7: T is for T-shirts and other light clothes.

Spring 8: I is for me—I love spring the most!

Spring 9: M is for a magical time of rebirth.

Spring 10: And E is for everything on this great
Earth.

All: We know each of you will have your own reasons
To enjoy the whole year and love all the seasons!

All: *(Sing: "Four Seasons." Assign four children to
stand and name one of the seasons when his or
her name is sung on the last verse.)*

All: Before we go our separate ways,
There's something we want to do.
We want to thank everyone who's helped,
And—especially—we thank you! *(Blow kisses to
audience)*

Make a Little Book

My Tree Through Four Seasons

Name _____

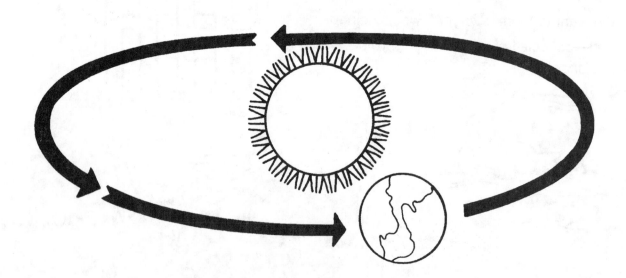

There are four seasons in the year
As Earth moves slowly around the sun.
Days grow longer then shorter again
And changing seasons always come.

1

Make a Little Book *(cont.)*

In spring the Earth begins to warm.
My tree sprouts tiny spring-green leaves.
Other living things wake up,
The grass and bears and flowers and bees.

2

In summer it is hot, hot, hot!
But my tree provides me shade.
Under big green leaves that block the sun,
I sit and drink cold lemonade.

3

Make a Little Book *(cont.)*

Cool autumn turns my tree's leaves colors—
Red and gold and orange and brown.
When my tree gets tired at last,
The leaves fall gently to the ground.

4

My tree just sleeps through wintertime,
Bare against the wind and snow.
But when the spring again returns,
It will again begin to grow.

5

Make a Little Book *(cont.)*

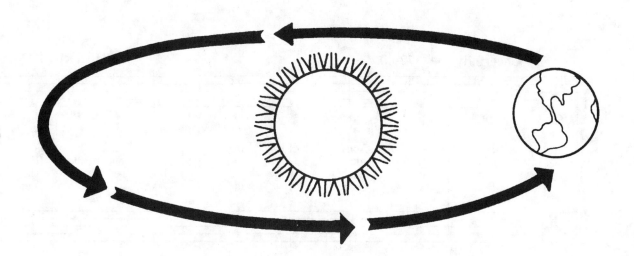

There are four seasons in the year
As Earth moves slowly around the sun.
Days grow longer then shorter again
And changing seasons always come.

6

This is a picture of my tree and me in my
favorite season.

7

Four Seasons of the Year

CHERRIL JONES

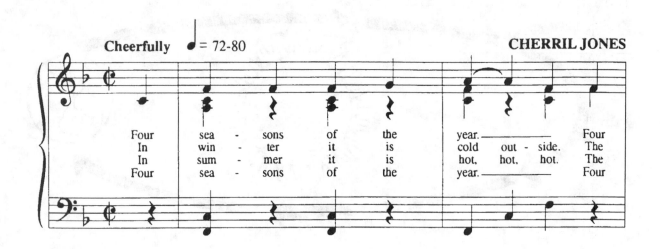

Four sea - sons of the year._____ Four
In win - ter it is cold out - side. The
In sum - mer it is hot, hot, hot. The
Four sea - sons of the year._____ Four

sea - sons of the year._____ The
plants and trees are rest - ing. In
sun shines bright on me._____ In
sea - sons of the year._____ Now

world is spin - ning
spring the world is
fall the leaves are
(Childs name)_____ stand and

'round_____ the sun so chang - es al - ways come._____
wak - ing up and lit - tle birds are nest - ing.
yel - low and red A won - der - ful sight to see.
tell_____ the rest the sea - son you like best._____

I Can Revolve and Rotate

Materials:

- Four balls (covered with yellow fabric or paper)
- Four flashlights
- Four construction paper outlines of the United States
- Masking tape

Directions:

1. Select an open area and make four slightly oval-shaped circles about eight feet in diameter.

2. Divide the class into four groups.

3. Model the activity, using volunteers.

   a. Put one student (sun) in the middle of the oval (orbit). Have him or her kneel and hold the yellow ball on top of his or her head. Remind the sun to always hold the ball and his or her body still because the sun never moves.

   b. Tape the U.S. pattern on the shirt front of a second student; this student is the Earth.

   c. Have the Earth stand on the orbit and lean his or her head in a bit to show the Earth's tilt.

   d. Have a third student hold a flashlight on top of the sun. This student is the sunlight. The sunlight will follow the Earth as it moves and tilts. (Stress that the sun doesn't move, but light comes from all around it all the time. Tell students that they will show the light all around by moving the flashlight.)

   e. Have Earth tilt a little and begin slowly rotating as he or she walks slowly around the orbit. Make sure the sunlight keeps his or her flashlight beam shining on Earth the whole time.

4. Have the four groups of students choose an orbit and act out the revolution and rotation of the Earth around the sun. Let each student in each group have an opportunity to be the sun, Earth, and sunlight.

5. When the activity is completed, use volunteers to show what would happen if the Earth didn't rotate. (The sun would shine only on one part of the Earth all the time.)

Weather Doll

58

Weather Doll Clothes Patterns

Summer

Weather Doll Clothes Patterns *(cont.)*

Autumn

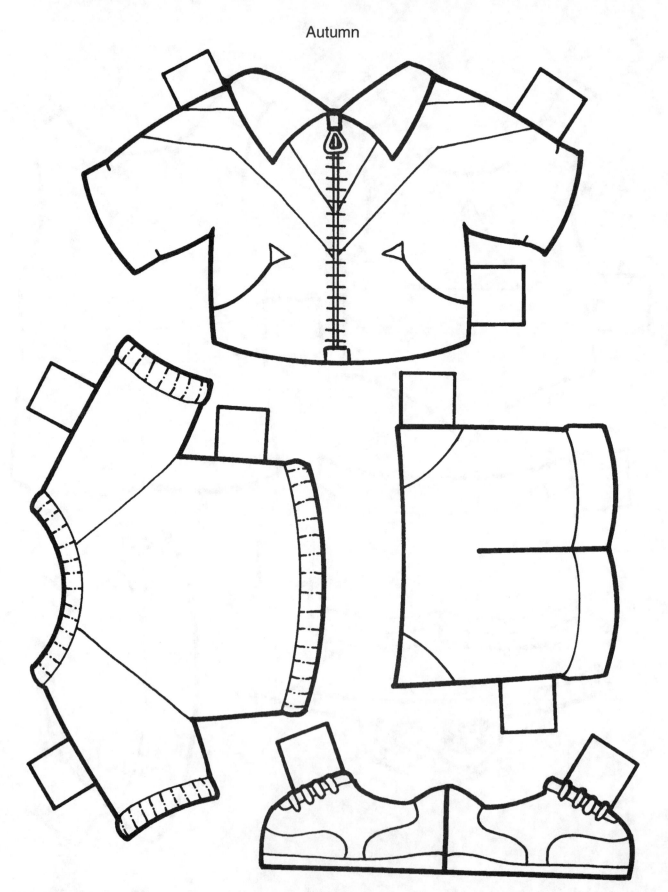

Weather Doll Clothes Patterns *(cont.)*

Winter

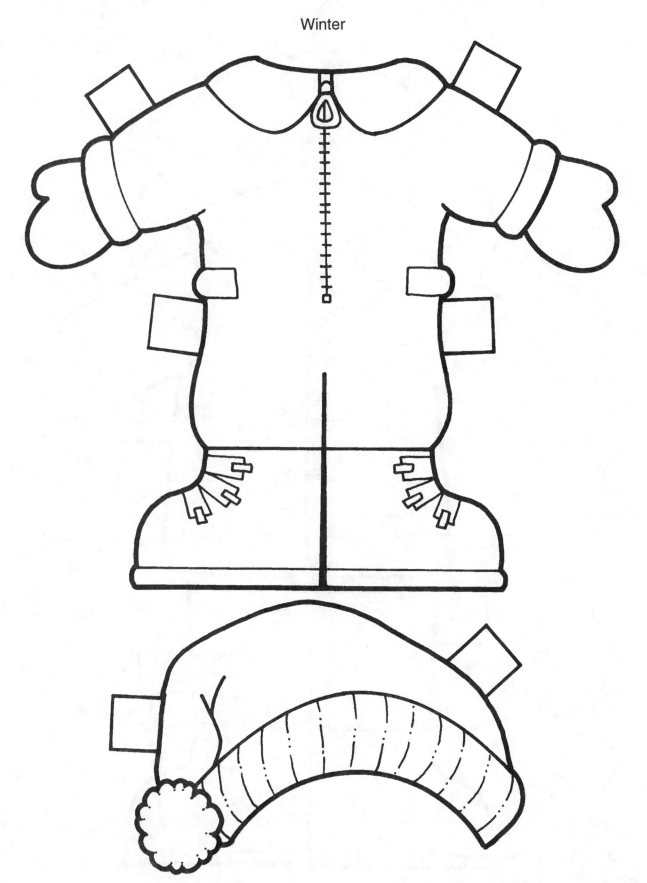

Weather Doll Clothes Patterns *(cont.)*

Spring

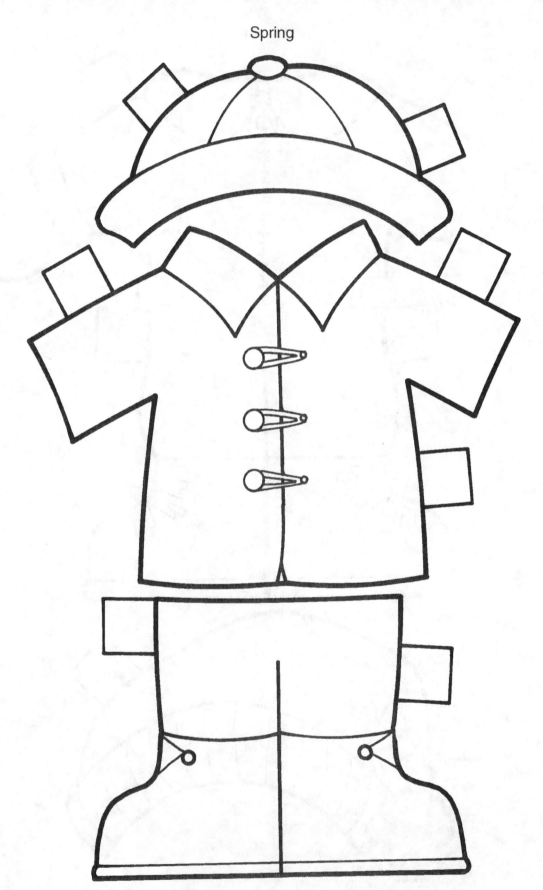

Tree Pattern

#0044 Science Explorations

Snowman Math

Lose a turn =

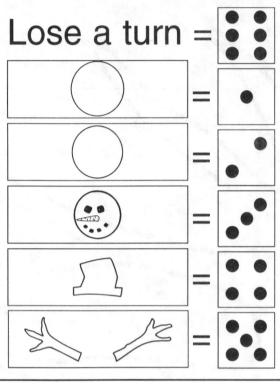

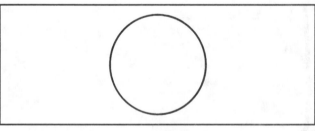

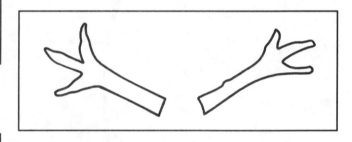

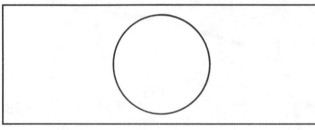

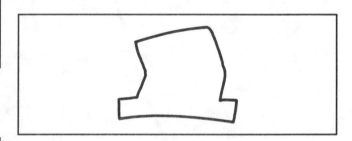

Parent Letter

Dear Parent,

Please come to our "Seasons" program. We promise you will have lots of fun— and maybe even learn some things, too!

Class: _____

_____

Where: _____

Date: _____

Time: _____

Sincerely,

_____

Four Seasons

Happily ♩ = 72-80

CHERRIL JONES

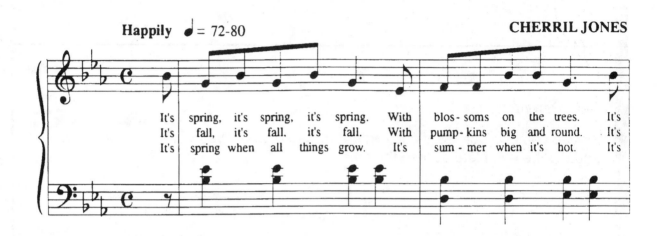

It's spring, it's spring, it's spring. With blos-soms on the trees. It's
It's fall, it's fall, it's fall. With pump-kins big and round. It's
It's spring when all things grow. It's sum-mer when it's hot. It's

spring, it's spring, it's spring. With birds and flow'rs and bees. It's
fall, it's fall, it's fall. With bright leaves on the ground. It's
fall when leaves turn red. And win - ter snows a - lot. It's

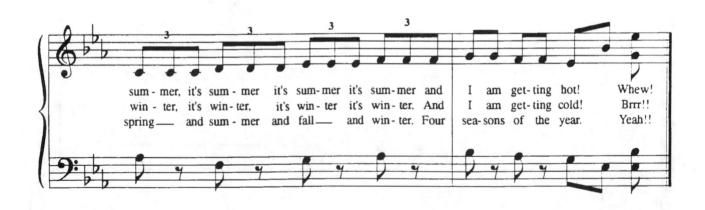

sum - mer, it's sum - mer it's sum - mer it's sum-mer and I am get-ting hot! Whew!
win - ter, it's win - ter, it's win - ter it's win-ter. And I am get-ting cold! Brrr!!
spring — and sum - mer and fall — and win - ter. Four sea-sons of the year. Yeah!!

The Spider

A spider's not an insect.
She's an arachnid—not a bug.
She's always looking out for food,
So don't give her a hug.

She sees a lot with her eight eyes,
And she bites with her strong jaws.
She's got sharp-pointed poison fangs
And eight legs—all with claws.

Her spinnerets make silken thread—
With some parts very sticky.
She hides away until her prey
Gets caught—then things get icky.

The insect struggles to get free,
But the spider hurries to it.
She wraps her meal up tight with silk,
And bites but doesn't chew it.

She slowly sucks the insect's blood.
To her that's very yummy.
And then with fuzzy legs she rubs
Her abdomen—her tummy!

And if her web is broken
Or torn in any way,
She'll get to work to fix it
To use another day.

Spiders

Presenting the Lessons

Objectives: Students will learn the body parts of a spider, how to compare and contrast spiders and insects, the two types of spiders, about webs and spiderlings, and how spiders can help us and can harm us.

Unit Poem and Little Book: "The Spider"

Lesson 1

Teach students the "Eency, Weency Spider" song and finger play.

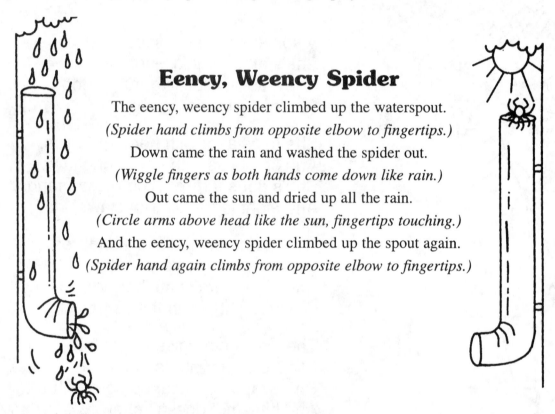

Eency, Weency Spider

The eency, weency spider climbed up the waterspout.
(Spider hand climbs from opposite elbow to fingertips.)
Down came the rain and washed the spider out.
(Wiggle fingers as both hands come down like rain.)
Out came the sun and dried up all the rain.
(Circle arms above head like the sun, fingertips touching.)
And the eency, weency spider climbed up the spout again.
(Spider hand again climbs from opposite elbow to fingertips.)

Discuss with students where they have seen spiders and what they know and think about spiders. Tell students to listen carefully as you read aloud the poem "The Spider" on page 67. Then ask them whether they learned anything about spiders from the poem that they didn't know before.

Elicit that the spider is an arachnid (verse 1), not an insect, or bug. Have students name some things they think are insects. If they say scorpions, ticks, or any kind of spider, tell them they have named an arachnid, not an insect. Tell students that arachnids have eight legs and insects have six.

Review the objectives, and tell students what they will learn about spiders. Have students assemble and color the Little Book on pages 76–79. Make a class Big Book from the Little Book (see suggestions on page 2). Display and read aloud the Big Book as students read along in their Little Books. Ask students what they learned about how a spider looks (verse 2).

Teach the body parts as you create a bulletin board with students using enlarged spider parts and labels from page 80. Explain each of the parts as you put them up.

Presenting the Lessons *(cont.)*

Part I of a Comparing Spider/Insect Body Parts outline is below. Part II follows in Lesson 2.

> I. Spider body has two main parts: the thorax and abdomen
>
>   A. Thorax—a spider doesn't have a separate head
>
>   1. Eyes—most spiders have eight eyes, but some have six, four, two, or none (place two large eyes on thorax, with six smaller eyes around the other two)
>
>   2. Two jaws—with two sharp, pointed fangs containing poison (place jaws and fangs on front of thorax)
>
>   3. Pedipalps—special feeling mouth parts that look like feelers or short legs (but are not either) that help the spider know what is around and help hold a bug down while spider bites it with its fangs (place close to and on each side of fangs)
>
>   4. Legs—eight, with little claws on the ends (place four legs on each side of thorax, two pairs pointing forward and two pairs pointing backward)
>
>   B. Abdomen—has a special job
>
>   1. Spinnerets—usually six organs used to produce the silk that comes from all spiders, though not all spiders make webs
>
>   2. Other organs—heart, digestive tract, etc.

Review the body parts with students and tell them they are going to make their very own spider. Present the activity sheet There's a Spider in My Kitchen! on page 81.

Curriculum Connections

Art: Make hand and foot spiders. Foot: Instruct students to make the spider body by tracing around their shoe onto black or brown construction paper. Draw and color eyes and fangs on the thorax (heel). Draw spinnerets on the abdomen (toe part). Cut out. Hand: Fold a second sheet of construction paper in half, and trace one hand on the folded paper. Cut out, making two hand patterns. Glue the hands behind the thorax, thumbs sticking forward to form the pedipalps and the fingers making the eight legs. Students may decorate with glitter, sequins, etc. Tape string to the backs of the spiders and hang from webs made of twine or a net that has been attached to the ceiling or corner of the classroom.

Creative Drama: Encourage students to pretend to be spiders. Have them "spider walk" around the room by walking on their hands and toes with their bodies arched.

Math: Divide the class into groups of four. Give each group two dice, 12 plastic spiders, and paper and pencil. Have students take turns being the secretary, the roller, the counter, and the spider checker. The roller rolls the dice, the counter counts the dots on the dice, the secretary records the number, and the spider counter counts the correct number of spiders. The entire group then counts the spiders aloud.

Presenting the Lessons *(cont.)*

Lesson 2

Read aloud the Big Book as students read along in their Little Books. Have them listen for the part of the poem that tells what a spider is not (verse 1). Tell students they are going to find out why a spider is not an insect or a bug.

Enlarge the Butterfly Pattern on page 82 onto poster board.

Part II of a Comparing Spider/Insect Body Parts outline.

II. Insect body has three main parts: head, thorax, abdomen

    A. Head—insect has separate head

        1. Two feelers, or antennae, used mainly for smelling

        2. Eyes—two main eyes

        3. Mouth

    B. Thorax

        1. Six legs attached to thorax

        2. Wings—most insects have wings, but some do not. Insects can have two or four wings.

    C. Abdomen—important organs, heart, digestive tract, etc.

Compare and contrast spiders and insects by drawing a Venn diagram on the chalkboard.

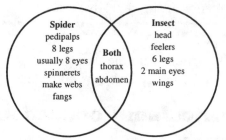

Reproduce a copy of Spider or Insect? (page 83) for each student and present the activity.
Tell students they will make insects—beautiful butterflies. Present the Eggs-tra Special Butterfly activity on page 84.

Curriculum Connections

Creative Drama: Encourage students to pretend to be insects. Have them "fly" around the room, flapping their "wings." Then divide the class into two groups and have them take turns beings spiders and insects.

Math: Play Make-a-Spider or Make-an-Insect game, page 85. Divide the class into two groups and name one group Spiders and the other Insects. Make game pieces by reproducing and laminating on poster board enough pieces for groups of four students. Each team needs a die and spider/insect body parts. Each time a player rolls the die, he or she may put a spider or insect part on the table. A player must first roll a 1 for the abdomen. Other parts may be added as the corresponding number on the die is thrown. When all of the spider/insect body parts are complete, each student will draw a picture of a spider/insect, using the body parts correctly. When a spider team finishes, it can trade places with an insect team, and vice versa.

Presenting the Lessons *(cont.)*

Patterning: Make a set of 24 Spider and Butterfly Cards (page 86) for each student. Reproduce three each of red, blue, yellow, and green spiders and butterflies. Put all 24 into an envelope for each student. Demonstrate how to pattern. For example, spider, butterfly, spider, butterfly; red spider, blue spider, yellow spider, etc.; green spider, green butterfly, red spider, red butterfly, etc. Keep the patterning packets to use throughout the year, making the patterns more difficult as students become more proficient.

Lesson 3

Read aloud the Big Book as students read along in their Little Books. Have them listen for the part of the poem that tells what special thing some spiders do to catch their favorite food—yummy insects (verses 3–5). Tell students they will learn about two kinds of spiders—those that make webs to catch insects and those that catch them in other ways.

Discuss the two kinds of spiders: wandering spiders and web builders. Use the Kinds of Spiders outline on page 87. Both kinds like to eat tasty insects for breakfast, lunch, and dinner, but they catch insects in different ways. Although both kinds make silk with their spinnerets, only the web builders use the silk to make webs to catch insects. The wandering spiders hunt and catch their insects without a web.

Take students on a walk around the school, looking for spider webs. If one is found, spray the web with three or four light coats of quick-drying clear spray lacquer. Let the lacquer dry after each coat. Place a piece of black, sturdy paper behind the web. Carefully cut the web free and catch it on the paper. Spray the web once again so it will stick to the paper. Display on a bulletin board or the science center. You may wish to find and mount several webs before your walk in case you don't find one on the walk.

Tell students they will pretend to be a web building spider. Present the Building Webs activity on page 88.

Curriculum Connections

Art: Have students make orb webs. Demonstrate on a square of black construction paper. With a piece of chalk, draw a line from one corner of the square to the opposite corner. Repeat on the other corners. Draw a line from the middle top to the middle bottom, crossing at the intersection. Repeat going from side to side. Beginning in the center of the web and working in a continuous circular direction, draw slightly curved sections that go from one straight line to the next. Go around the web four or five times, spacing the curved lines fairly widely apart. Show how to use a damp paper towel or tissue to erase chalk if a mistake is made. Demonstrate tracing the chalk lines with glue and applying glitter.

Phonics: Reproduce a Spider Begins with "S" phonics worksheet on page 89 for each student. Have students draw a line from the "S" in the web to each picture that begins with the sound of *s*.

Presenting the Lessons *(cont.)*

Phonics and Creative Drama: Sing and dance to the tune of "London Bridge." Use the *s* sound, not the letter name.

Spider begins with s, s, s.
S, s, s.
S, s, s.
Spider begins with s, s, s,
And spiders catch insects!

Have three students make a "web" by joining hands and holding them high as they stand in a circle. Have the students step apart so the "web threads" (their hands and arms) are high enough for other students to duck under and walk in and out between them. As you all sing, have the rest of the students walk in a line into and out of the "web." When you sing "And spiders catch insects," have the web come down and catch the student who is inside. That person then trades places with one of the web students, and the game continues.

Lesson 4

Tell students they will learn about baby spiders. Baby spiders begin their lives as tiny eggs in an egg sac. (Show a picture of an egg sac.) Sometimes there may be only one or two eggs in an egg sac, but the large spiders can have as many as 10,000 eggs in just one sac. The mother spider leaves the eggs soon after she has laid them.

When baby spiders first hatch, they are called *spiderlings*. They stay in the egg sac because they cannot see or move. But after a few days, the spiderlings are big enough to come out of the egg sac. Sometimes these tiny spiderlings work together to build a web called a nursery web. They stay there until they get hungry.

When they are ready to go find food, they climb to the top of a plant or blade of grass. Then, standing high on their legs with their spinnerets pointing up, they spin a few thin threads of silk. With the silk still attached to their abdomens, they wait for a breeze to blow. The breeze catches the silk, and the spiderlings sail out into the air. This is called *ballooning*. In this way, spiderlings move to a new spot where they can live and find food. Teach students the song and finger play to the tune of "Rock-a-Bye Baby."

Fly away, spiderling, from a tree top. (wiggle fingers)
When the wind blows, from silk you will drop. (clap on "drop")
Then you will find an insect to eat. (cup hands together)
An insect delicious, juicy, and sweet. (rub stomach)

Reproduce a Spiderlings sheet (page 90) for each student. Have them color and cut out the spiderlings. Tell them that spiderlings need an egg sac and that they are going to make one for their spiderlings. Present the Spiderling Egg Sac activity on page 91.

Presenting the Lessons *(cont.)*

Curriculum Connections

Phonics: Use one of the spiderling patterns from page 90 and trace it on black or brown construction paper. Cut out enough spiderlings for each student to have one. Glue small pictures (some beginning with *s* and some not) on one side of each spiderling and laminate. Make an egg sac out of a white paper bag. Place the spiderlings inside.

With masking tape, tightly secure a five- or six-foot (2 m) piece of string in a corner of the room where students may readily reach it. Pin various lengths of string on it with clothespins. Have cellophane tape handy with which to hang the spiderlings that have the *s* sound. Make a small nursery web with net or string.

Have students choose a spiderling from the egg sac and determine if the picture on the underside begins with the s sound. If it does, the spiderling may dangle from the thread. If it doesn't, it must be put on the nursery web. **Note:** This activity can be modified for math and spelling activities.

Math: Reproduce Spiderling/Web Match-Up patterns on page 92. Write addition or subtraction equations on the web and the corresponding answers on the spiderlings' bodies. Cut out and laminate. Tell students the spiderlings have gotten lost from their nursery webs. They will help the spiderlings get back to the right web by matching the addition or subtraction problem on the web with the correct answer on the spiderling.

Lesson 5

Recite the poem "Little Miss Muffet" (*The Real Mother Goose*, Rand McNally & Company, 1916).

Little Miss Muffet
Sat on her tuffet,
Eating her curds and whey.
Along came a spider
And sat down beside her,
Scaring Miss Muffet away!

Ask students how they feel about spiders. Explain that many people are afraid of spiders. Ask students why they think that is so. Tell them that most spiders won't hurt us and many help us in a very important way.

Spiders eat pesky insects that damage our yards, plants, gardens, and food crops. We need spiders to eat these insects so there won't be so many. This is the way nature keeps the animal world in balance. Animals that kill other animals for food are called *predators*. The animals they eat are called their *prey*. Spiders are predators to their prey, insects.

Spiders are prey, too. They make a tasty meal for many animals, such as frogs, birds, small mammals, and even some insects (especially wasps). Some kinds of spiders eat other spiders. Spiders have another enemy—people. We don't eat spiders, but many people kill them because they don't like them in their homes.

Presenting the Lessons *(cont.)*

Spiders try to stay away from people and other enemies and have clever ways to stay alive. They like dark corners of houses and garages and barns—places where people do not sweep or clean very often. They generally will not bite unless they feel they are in danger of being trapped and cannot get away.

When an enemy comes near, most spiders will run and hide in dark places. Camouflage is a way that spiders can hide. They find a place that is about the same color as they are.

Some spiders spin a thread and fall. Then they use the thread to climb back up again when it is safe. Others pretend to be dead. They will fall on their backs to the ground, curl their legs up tight, and lie very still until the danger has passed. But the most amazing of all are the spiders that lose a leg! If the spider is not an adult yet, the leg will grow back again.

Almost all spiders have poison and can bite. Spiders use the poison to paralyze and kill their prey. When spiders bite people, they put poison in them, but the poison is not usually strong enough to hurt us badly. Spider bites can give us a bump, a sting, an itch, or a rash. If you think you have been bitten by a spider, call an adult right away.

There are two kinds of poisonous spiders whose poison can make people very sick and even kill them. A black widow is very poisonous. If it bites a person, its poison can cause death. A black widow has a very small thorax and its abdomen is shaped like a marble. It is very shiny black. If it is on a web and you can see its underside, you can tell a black widow by a red mark shaped like an hourglass. Stay away from shiny black spiders!

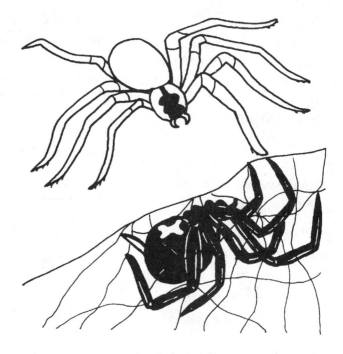

The brown recluse spider is also very poisonous. It has a brown body with a dark violin-shaped mark on its top side. It is about the same size and lives in the same places as a black widow. They both like to live in dark garages, piles of trash, under furniture, and in the folds of clothing.

Tell students that since it's hard to tell which spiders can hurt us, it is very important for them to not touch spiders and for adults to be very careful when handling them. Tell students when they find a spider to let adults know so they can capture the spider and take it outside.

Curriculum Connections

Speaking, Listening, Reading, Writing, Organizing, Drama, Art: Brainstorm with students the new and interesting things they have learned about spiders. Have them think of the two most interesting facts they discovered. (Students will write about these and use them in a puppet show.) Present the Spider Puppet activity on page 93.

Presenting the Lessons *(cont.)*

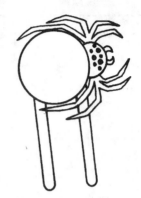

Put on a puppet show using the spider puppets. Create a stage (web) from a box covered with a net. Divide the class into small groups for planning and presenting their most interesting facts to the rest of the class. Have students display their spiders on the web stage as they present their fascinating facts.

Lesson 6

Take your class to a nature or science museum or have someone from the museum bring spider and insect collections to the class. If this is not possible, take the class to the playground or nearby park to look for spiders and insects.

Have a Party

Let students make spider hats to wear to the party. Enlarge several Spider Hat Patterns (page 94) for students to trace onto black construction paper and cut out. Overlap and glue the wedge-shaped edges to make a wide, cone. Fan-fold the eight legs. Glue four legs on each side toward the front. Cut eight small circles out of green construction paper for the eyes. Have students glue them on the front on their hats. Give them plain paper cups and let them draw webs on the outside with black crayons or markers.

Serve "Spider Bites." Cookie dough or prepared cookies can be used for the spiders' bodies. Have students place two cookies on a paper plate to form the body (abdomen and thorax). Provide other edible goodies for additional body parts, such as string licorice, thin peppermint sticks, nuts, pretzel sticks, small candies, sprinkles, chocolate chips, shredded coconut, canned chocolate frosting, etc. Have students make a "yummy" spider to eat. They can drink "spider silk" (milk) from their "web" cups.

     #0044 Science Explorations

Make a Little Book

The Spider

Name _____

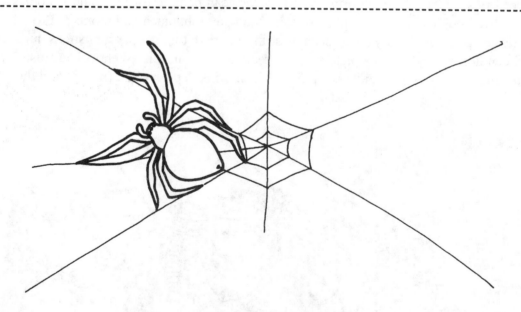

A spider's not an insect.
She's an arachnid—not a bug.
She's always looking out for food,
So don't give her a hug.

1

Make a Little Book *(cont.)*

She sees a lot with her eight eyes,
And she bites with her strong jaws.
She's got sharp-pointed poison fangs
And eight legs—all with claws.

2

Her spinnerets make silken thread—
With some parts very sticky.
She hides away until her prey
Gets caught—then things get icky.

3

Make a Little Book (cont.)

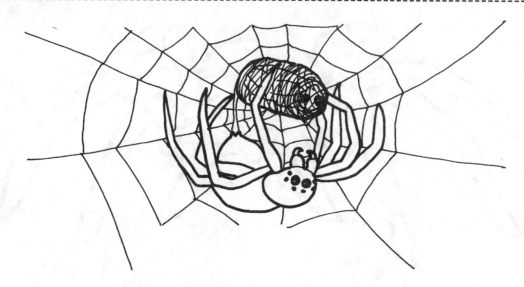

The insect struggles to get free,
But the spider hurries to it.
She wraps her meal up tight with silk,
And bites but doesn't chew it.

4

She slowly sucks the insect's blood.
To her that's very yummy.
And then with fuzzy legs she rubs
Her abdomen—her tummy!

5

Make a Little Book *(cont.)*

And if her web is broken
Or torn in any way,
She'll get to work to fix it
To use another day.

6

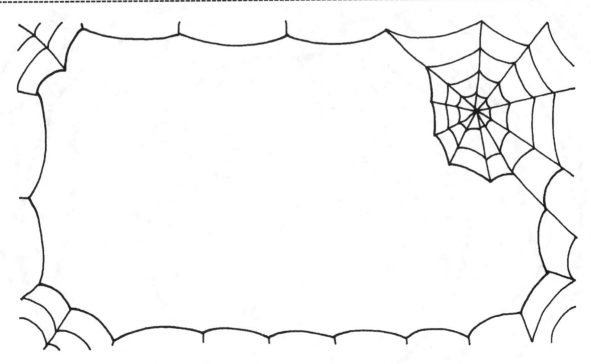

Here is a picture of a spider on a web.

7

Spiders

Spider Parts

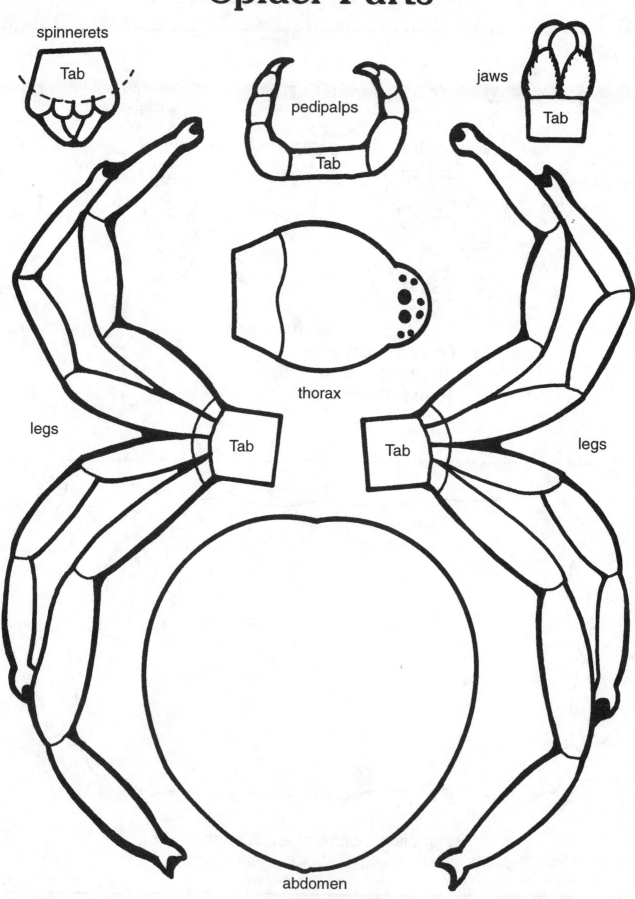

© Teacher Created Materials, Inc.

There's a Spider in My Kitchen!

Materials:

- Body—paper plates, sections (cups) of an egg carton, clay, or Styrofoam balls
- Parts—assortment of kitchen things, such as straws, toothpicks, pipe cleaners, craft sticks, pretzels, aluminum foil, small elbow macaroni, cinnamon sticks, candy sprinkles and beads, dried beans, rice, small assorted candies, etc.

Directions:

1. Have students assemble the two body parts and attach eight pipe cleaner legs to the thorax.

2. Then have students use any of the kitchen things to complete the spider by adding eyes, fangs, pedipalps, and spinnerets.

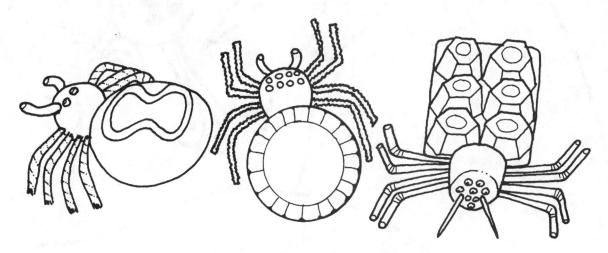

Flour Clay Recipe

Materials:

- 2 cups (500 mL) flour
- 1 cup (250 mL) water
- 1 cup (250 mL) salt
- 2 tablespoons (30 mL) alum
- Food coloring
- Bowl

Directions:

1. Knead all the ingredients together in a bowl until the mixture is smooth and pliable.

2. Knead in the food coloring.

Recipe Tips:

- Wear rubber gloves when kneading in the food coloring to prevent staining your hands.
- Separate the dough into balls and knead in different colors of food coloring to make different-colored clay.

Butterfly Pattern

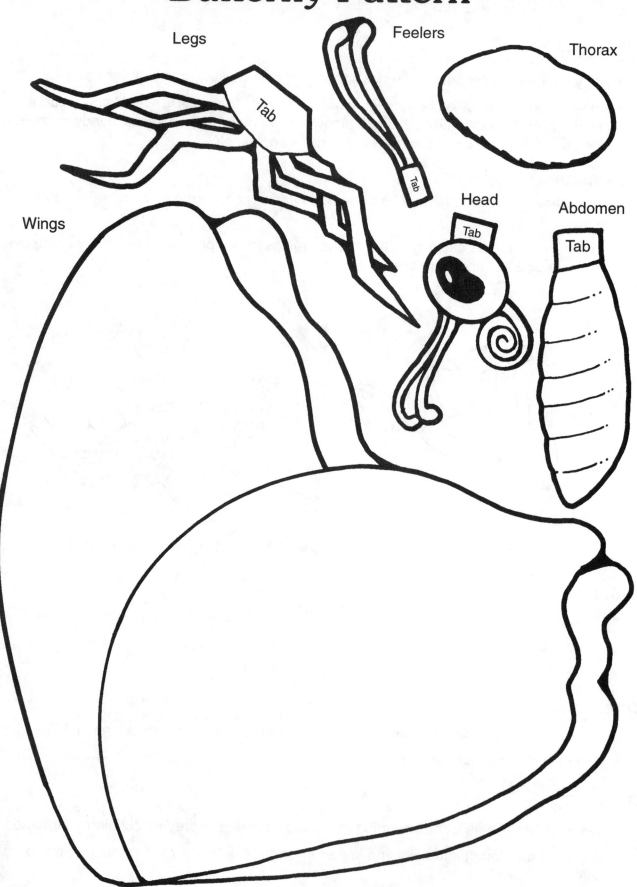

Legs

Feelers

Thorax

Wings

Head

Abdomen

Tab

Tab

Tab

Tab

Spider or Insect?

Study the spider and insect and record what you see.

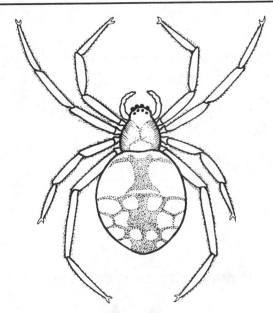

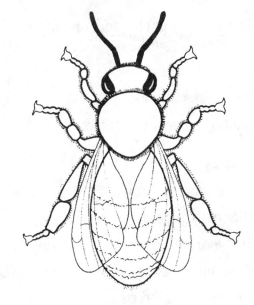

| **Spider** | **Insect** |

Write the number you see.

1. _____ main body parts

2. _____ legs

3. _____ pedipalps

4. _____ feelers, or antennae

5. _____ eyes

6. _____ wings

7. _____ fangs

Write "yes" or "no."

8. Do you see spinnerets? _____

9. Do you see a head? _____

10. Do you see a thorax? _____

11. Do you see an abdomen? _____

Write the number you see.

1. _____ main body parts

2. _____ legs

3. _____ pedipalps

4. _____ feelers, or antennae

5. _____ eyes

6. _____ wings

7. _____ fangs

Write "yes" or "no."

8. Do you see spinnerets? _____

9. Do you see a head? _____

10. Do you see a thorax? _____

11. Do you see an abdomen? _____

Eggs-tra Special Butterfly

Materials:

- Egg carton cut into sections of three
- Pipe cleaners
- Toothpicks or wire
- Tissue paper (assorted colors)

- Black marker
- Colored markers or construction paper scraps
- Glue
- Scissors

Directions:

1. Use the egg carton section as the insect body.
2. Attach six pipe cleaners as legs.
3. Use wire or toothpicks for antennae.
4. Make tissue-paper wings, using the black marker to draw patterns on the wings.
5. Add construction paper scraps for eyes and mouth.

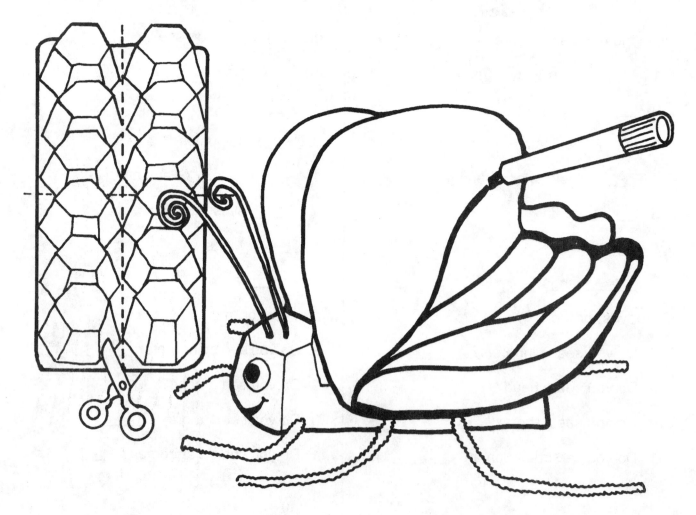

Make-a-Spider or Make-an-Insect

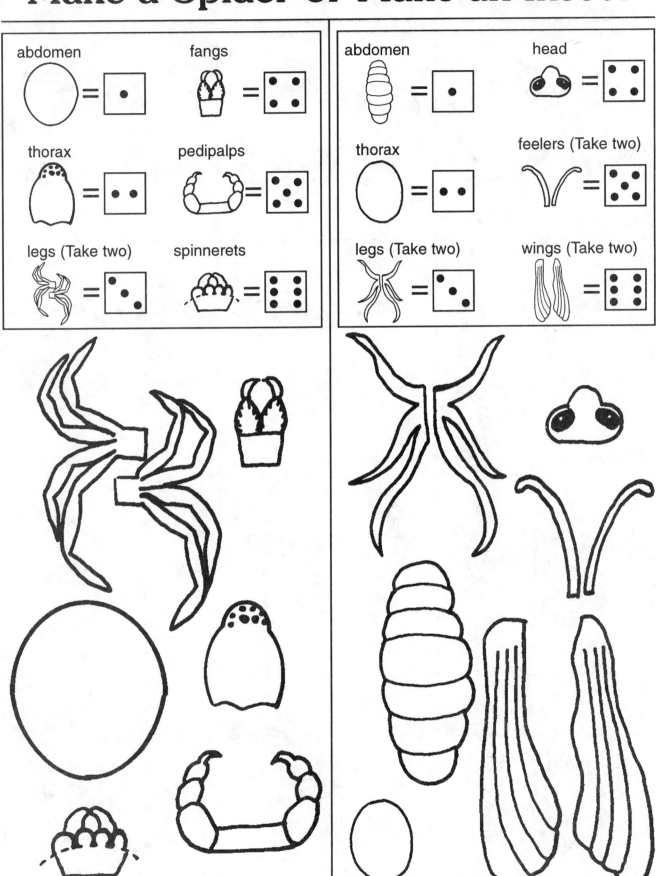

Spider and Butterfly Cards

Kinds of Spiders

I. Wandering Spiders

    A. Live on the ground under rocks, in trees, or in burrows to hunt for insects

    B. Have powerful jaws to grab and hold on to insects

    C. Have sharp, poisonous fangs to paralyze or kill insects

    D. Have hairy bodies to help them find their way along the ground

    E. Have very good, big eyes to help them get away from enemies

    F. Examples:

        1. Tiger spiders—follow insects and leap on them

        2. Some run across the top of water and grab insects sitting on top; can also dive down into the water

        3. Spitting spider—spits sticky glue from its fangs to stick insects to the ground so they can't get away

        4. Jumping spiders—have four large eyes and can see better than any other spider; jump from far away and land on insects

        5. Trap-door spiders—dig a small hole in the ground and use their silk to make a door on the top that opens and closes; when insects walk on the trap door, the spiders feel the vibrations and quickly push the door open and catch the insect

II. Web Builders

    A. Have tiny eyes that do not see as well as wandering spiders

    B. Make different types and shapes of webs—triangular, flat, tunnel-shaped, round, and some with silk going in every direction

    C. Use webs to catch insects; wait patiently for their dinner

    D. Have spinnerets that spin thin or thick, slippery or sticky silk

    E. Have long, sensitive legs that feel web vibrate when an insect gets caught in it

    F. Catch dinner

        1. Wrap insect in silk until it looks like a cocoon, to keep insect from escaping or stinging

        2. Can save the insect until they are hungry

        3. Use fangs to inject special liquid into insect to make it soft

        4. Suck only the insect's blood and body fluids

        5. Push the dead insect out of and repair the web

Building Webs

Materials:

- Styrofoam or wood block
- Wax paper
- Thin nails
- String or yarn
- Liquid starch
- Bowl
- Paper towels
- Enlarged web pattern

Directions:

1. Place web pattern and wax paper on the Styrofoam or wood block.

2. Push or hammer nails into the tips (nail points) on the web.

3. Cut string or yarn into manageable lengths.

4. Pour liquid starch into the bowl.

5. Cover pieces of string or yarn completely with starch, one at a time, and string them from the outer nails to the center nail, wrapping the ends around both points.

6. With more pieces of string or yarn dipped in starch, string the pieces between the nails in the pattern shown.

7. Allow the webs to dry overnight.

8. Carefully remove the nails and hang the stiffened webs around the room.

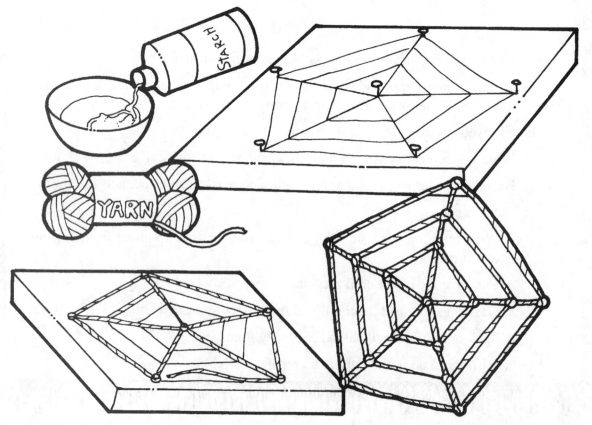

Spider Begins With "S"

Spiderlings

90

Spiderling Egg Sac

Materials:

- Small white paper bags
- Spiderlings (page 90), cut out and colored
- String or rubber bands
- Scrap paper or newspaper
- Glue

Directions:

1. Divide the class into pairs and give each student a white paper bag.
2. Have students blow into their bags to open them and put 4–5 spiderlings inside.
3. Then have them stuff some crumpled paper inside.
4. Tell students to ask their partners to hold the bag openings closed while they secure them with string or a rubber band.
5. Have students glue the remainder of their spiderlings on the outside of the egg sac.
6. Display the egg sacs in the classroom.

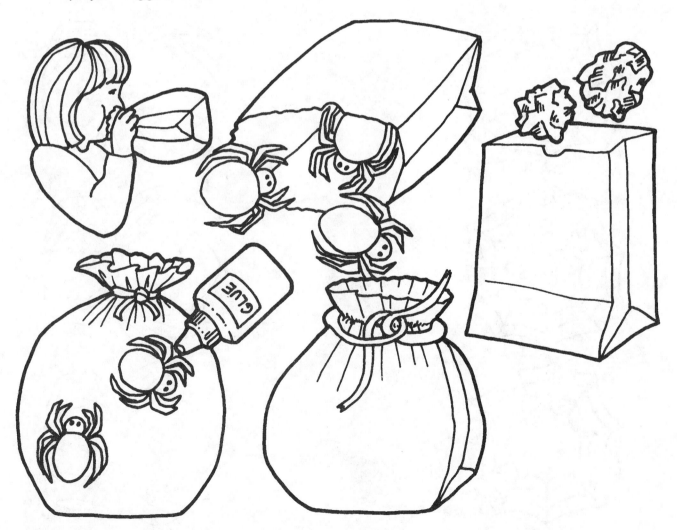

Spiderling/Web Match-Up

92

Spider Puppet

Materials:

- Spider pattern below
- Construction paper
- Crayons or markers
- Glue or stapler
- Craft sticks

Directions:

1. Reproduce a spider pattern for each student on white or manila construction paper.
2. Have each student color and decorate one side of the spider.
3. Have each student cut out a spider.
4. Help students write their two interesting facts on the underside of the spider.
5. Glue or staple two craft sticks on the back side of the spider for students to hold the spider puppets through the web (net).

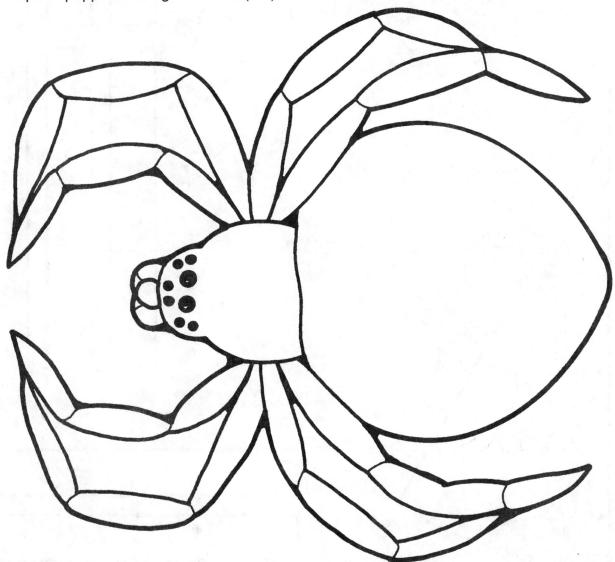

Spider Hat Pattern

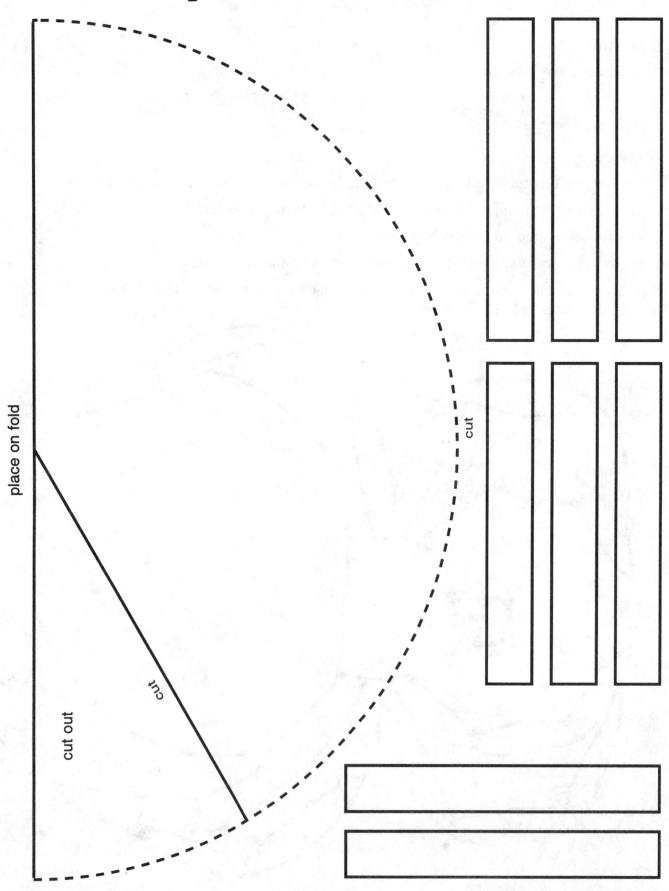

place on fold

cut

cut

cut out

Magnets

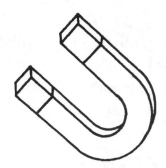

All magnets are attractive,
In whatever shape and size.
They pull some objects toward
them
With their ends and all their
sides.

There are magnets shaped like
rods and bars,
And some look like a horseshoe.
Each kind has poles—a north
and south.
The south is red; the north is
blue.

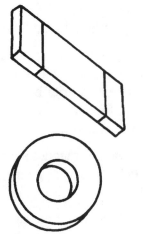

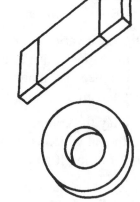

Magnets work through lots of
things
Such as water, sand, and air.
They can move a compass
through a book
As though it were not there!

A magnet has magnetic force
And a strong magnetic field.
But its force can also be shut
down
With a nonmagnetic shield.

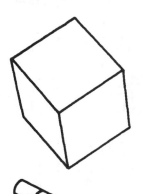

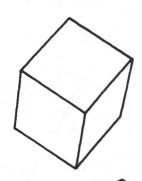

Magnets pull things made of iron,
But it's sometimes hard to tell
Which things a magnet will attract
And which it will repel.

Magnets push away—repel—
Or pull toward—attract.
And though they seem like
magic,
They're a scientific fact.

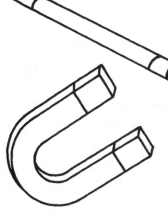

Magnets

Presenting the Lessons

Objectives: Students will learn about magnets—what they are, kinds of magnets, what magnets attract, uses of magnets, where magnets are found, and that the Earth is a giant magnet.

Unit Poem and Little Book: "Magnets"

Lesson 1

Read aloud the poem "Magnets" on page 95. Review the objectives, and tell students that they are going to learn about magnets. Have students assemble and color the Little Book (pages 103–106). Make a class Big Book from the Little Book (see suggestions on page 2). Display and read aloud the Big Book as students read along in their Little Books.

Display a variety of magnets: horseshoe, U-shaped, bar, rod, block, and ring. If possible, obtain a piece of lodestone. Also bring in a compass. Use Just the Facts on page 107 to give students a brief history of magnets and magnetism. Brainstorm with students what they already know about magnets and magnetism.

Display the compass. Use the bar magnet and the compass to learn which end of the bar magnet is north and which is south. Mark the north pole blue and the south pole red by attaching masking tape and coloring it with crayons or markers.

Suspend the bar magnet by attaching a rubber band to each end. Then tie one string between the two rubber bands and another string to the middle of the first string. Suspend the magnet so it swings freely.

When the magnet stops moving, have a volunteer choose one of the other types of magnets you have gathered. Have him or her choose an end of the magnet and bring it close to the north pole of the bar magnet. Observe what happens. Elicit from the class what pole the volunteer directed toward the bar magnet. (If it repelled, it was the same pole, north. If it attracted, it was the south pole.) Allow the volunteer to paint the correct poles of his or her magnet red and blue. Continue with this until all magnets have the poles marked north (blue) and south (red). Then ask the volunteers to test their magnets with each other to determine how magnets attract or repel. Reproduce Poles Apart on page 108 for students and have them record what they learned.

Reproduce Like or Unlike on page 109 for each student, and have them complete the activity sheet.

Presenting the Lessons *(cont.)*

Curriculum Connection

Art: Review the different types of magnets with students. Provide a clothes hanger for each student. Gather string and paper clips. Reproduce Magnet Patterns on page 110 and give one to each student. Have them color, label the poles, and cut out the patterns. Have students attach a small piece of magnetic tape onto each pattern. Have students cut a piece of string for each pattern and attach one end to the hanger and a paper clip to the other. Then have students make a Magnet Mobile by hanging the patterns to the paper clips. This can be adapted for seasons, spider body parts, or other units of study.

Math: Give students a Magnet Hunt activity sheet on page 111. Have them take it home and complete it. Tell them to return the sheet to school, and have students share the results of their magnet hunt with the class. Write on the chalkboard all the places magnets were found, keep a tally, and draw a bar graph of the magnet hunt for class discussion.

Lesson 2

Display and read aloud the Big Book as students read along in their Little Books. Discuss with students that they now know that magnets can attract or repel each other. Ask them whether they think magnets can attract or repel other things. Brainstorm with students what things magnets may attract and repel.

Gather a strong magnet and an assortment of small objects that are and are not magnetic, such as paper clips, nails, coins, aluminum foil, plastic, wood, fabric, pins, needles, and screws. Reproduce an Attraction Action work sheet (page 112) for each student. Ask one volunteer at a time to come to the front of the room and choose an item. Ask him or her to predict whether the object is magnetic or not; ask the class whether it agrees or disagrees. Then have the volunteer test the object with a magnet. Have the class record the results on their papers.

Tell students they will learn about magnetic strength. Reproduce a Magnetic Muscle work sheet (page 113) for each student. Discuss the different types of magnets they know about—horseshoe, bar, those for a refrigerator, etc. Ask them whether they think all magnets have the same strength. Using an assortment of magnets, 20 small nails, and 20 small paper clips, lead the class in a hands-on comparison of magnetic strength.

On the chalkboard, write the names of six or seven types of magnets that you have gathered: rod, bar, block, horseshoe, refrigerator, U-shaped, ring. Have the class predict the strength of the magnets and record the list on their charts, writing the name of the strongest type of magnet as number 1 and so on to the weakest. Then put the nails in one pile on your desk and the paper clips in another. Have a volunteer come to the desk and choose the magnet they predicted would be the strongest.

Presenting the Lessons *(cont.)*

Then ask the student (and the class) to predict whether the magnet will pick up more paper clips or more nails. Have the student stick one end of the magnet in either pile. Have him or her carefully lift the magnet out of the pile and count the number of objects that cling to it. Have the class record the number in the correct column. Ask another volunteer to do the same with the same magnet, only in the other object pile. Have the class record their findings. Continue until all the magnets have been used with both sets of objects.

Curriculum Connection

Phonics: Enlarge, cut out, and laminate the Garage Pattern on page 114. Display it on the front of a box so that the door is open. Laminate and cut out the Car Patterns on page 115. Gather small pictures of some things that begin with *m* and some that don't. Glue or tape a paper clip on the back of each car. Review the *m* sound with students. Have volunteers come to the front and choose a car. If the picture on it begins with the *m* sound, allow the student to use a bar magnet to "drive" the car into the garage. If the picture does not begin with the *m* sound, have students "drive" the car on down the "road" (away from the garage).

Lesson 3

Read aloud the Big Book as students read along in their Little Books. Remind students that the force field around a magnet is called the *magnetic field*. Ask students where around a magnet they think the magnetic field is the strongest. Tell them they will learn more about this area where a magnet's force attracts or repels objects.

Gather some coarse iron filings, two same-sized bar magnets with their poles marked, a piece of thin cardboard, and two books. (If you cannot find iron filings, put some steel wool into a plastic bag and cut it into small pieces. Wear safety goggles and be careful not to let filings fly into your eyes or mouth.)

Ask students to predict whether or not the north end of the magnet will attract or repel the filings. Dip the north pole of one bar magnet into the filings and pull it up slowly, with the filings hanging on to it. Then carefully put that magnet and filings aside. Ask students to predict whether the south pole of the magnet will attract or repel filings. Take the other magnet and dip the south pole of it into the filings. Pull it up slowly.

Still holding the magnet with south pole filings, pick up the magnet with filings stuck on the north pole. Ask students to predict what will happen when you bring the ends together. Slowly bring the magnets' two opposite poles together. The magnetic fields around the unlike poles attract and join together, and the iron filings are held in the magnetic field. Pull the two magnets a short distance apart; the filings will hang in the air.

Presenting the Lessons *(cont.)*

Do this procedure again, but this time attach the filings to the north poles of both magnets. Ask students to predict what will happen when you bring the ends together. Do it; the magnetic fields repel, and the filings push away from each other.

Distribute to each student a Magnetic Field Map on page 116. Make a bridge with the two books and cardboard. Sprinkle the iron filings onto the top of the cardboard. Using a magnet under the cardboard, show students how you can move the filings around to make different patterns. Tap the cardboard gently to scatter the filings. Then put one bar magnet under the cardboard and tap the cardboard gently until the filings arrange themselves into a pattern. Have students observe and draw a picture of what they see.

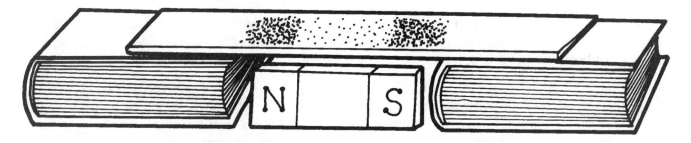

Do this twice more, each time creating a new pattern and having students draw on their field maps what they see. Use both bar magnets. First, put both bar magnets under the cardboard with unlike poles close together. Then, put both bar magnets under the cardboard with like poles close together.

Have each student hold a bar magnet in one hand. In the other hand, have him or her hold a paper clip over the magnet. Have the student drop the paper clip and notice where it is attracted. Then have students lay a pile of nails or paper clips on a desk. Then have them place a bar magnet horizontally over the pile and observe where most of the objects are attracted.

Curriculum Connections

Art: Supply several strong magnets and a variety of small magnetic objects. Allow students to create a "magnetic" sculpture.

Glue the Iron Man face pattern on page 117 to the bottom of a box. Put a cup of iron filings in the box, then cover and tape plastic wrap securely around the top and sides of the box. Cover the sides with contact paper or construction paper. Students will use a magnet through the bottom of the box to attract filings to make hair, eyebrows, mustache, and beard of "Iron Man."

Phonics: Have students play "Fishing for the *m* Sound." Make a fishing pole by attaching a string to a stick and tying a magnet to the end of the string. Trace a simple fish pattern on different-colored construction paper, glue on some pictures that begin with the *m* sound and some that don't, and laminate. Use magnetic tape or punch a hole for the fishes' mouths, and put a large paper clip through them. Place all the fish in a blue box. Have groups of students take turns fishing for the *m* pictures on the fish. If a student hooks an *m* fish, he or she may keep it and fish again. If not, the fish should be placed by the "pond" to be thrown back after all fish are caught, and the student passes the pole to the next student. The student who catches the most *m* fish wins.

Presenting the Lessons *(cont.)*

Lesson 4

Read aloud the Big Book as students read along in their Little Books. Ask students what the poem tells about how magnets work through nonmagnetic things (verses 3 and 4). Discuss with students what they have learned about magnets: magnets have an invisible force called *magnetism*; magnetism is strongest at the poles of magnets; magnetism attracts or repels certain objects; and magnetic force passes through the air to attract a magnetic object.

Tell students that air is not magnetic, yet magnetic force works through it. Elicit from students that magnetic force also works through nonmagnetic cardboard. Tell students they will learn more about when magnetic force works through other nonmagnetic substances—and when it doesn't.

Reproduce a Buried Treasure chart (page 118) for each student. Gather an assortment of magnetic objects (key, paper clip, small car, bobby pins, etc.) and an assortment of magnets. Make sure you have access to a sandbox or sand table.

Bury the objects lightly under just enough sand so that they cannot be seen. Divide the class into groups and tell them teams will be going on a treasure hunt. The only rule is they have to use a magnet to find their buried treasures. Give each student a magnet, and allow them to search for one treasure. Have students record the objects as each is found (attracted by the magnet).

As an alternate to this activity, provide iron filings, a small jar of sand, and a magnet. Shake the iron filings up in the sand and allow students to extract the filings from the sand with the magnet.

Ask students whether they think magnets will work through water. Gather a clear plastic cup, water, a paper clip, and a magnet for each student. Have each student half-fill his or her cup with water and drop in the paper clip. Tell students they must get the paper clip out of the water without putting their hands in the cup, dumping out the water, or getting their fingers wet.

Gather a strong magnet, a book, and a compass. Ask students whether they think a magnet will attract a compass needle through a book. Set up the book with the compass on one side. Challenge volunteers to use the magnet on the other side of the book to make the compass needle move.

Now add another book to the first, and test. Add one book at a time and test the magnetic force through them with the magnet and compass. Elicit from students that the force gets weaker as more books are added. Tell students that although nonmagnetic substances sometimes do not interfere with the magnetic force, they can also create a magnetic shield that stops the magnetic force.

Presenting the Lessons *(cont.)*

Tell students that although magnetism can be useful, sometimes it can be a nuisance. For example, if a person is working with a strong magnet and is wearing a watch, the magnetism may affect the watch by slowing it or stopping it. If there are machines nearby, such as computers, with steel or iron parts, a magnet may also interfere with their functions. Explain that the way to stop the damaging effects of magnetism is with a magnetic shield.

Elicit from students that a magnetic shield is made of nonmagnetic material. Tell students they will be using different nonmagnetic materials to see whether they can be used as a magnetic shield. Gather a bar magnet, a large paper clip, a ruler, a large piece of paper, and several pieces of the following: paper, cloth, plastic, cardboard, wire screen, aluminum foil.

Reproduce a Magnetic Shield Observation Chart on page 119 for each student. Assemble the experiment by taping the ruler onto the edge of the paper. Lay the paper clip on the paper at the zero end of the ruler. Move the bar magnet in toward the paper clip from the other end of the ruler. Note the distance when the paper clip begins to move toward the magnet. Have students record the distance on their charts. Then ask volunteers to come to the desk and cover the end of the magnet with a piece of one of the materials and test the attraction. Have them note the distance between the paper clip and magnet when the paper clip starts to move. Add more layers of the same material and test. Have students record their results. Continue with all the nonmagnetic materials.

Curriculum Connections

Art: Have students use magnets to paint. Gather magnetic objects, tempera paints, white paper, a shallow glass baking dish, and a strong magnet. Divide the students into pairs. Have one student put the white paper into the baking dish. Have the painter student put the magnetic objects into different colors of tempera paints to coat them and then place them on the paper. Have the helper student hold the baking dish while the painter uses the magnet to move the paint-covered objects around on the paper to create a painting. Let all the students paint a picture.

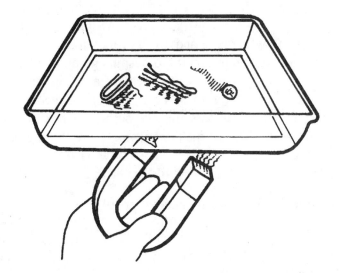

Classification: Have students fold a piece of construction paper in half. On one half, have them write "Magnetic Things," and on the other half, "Nonmagnetic Things." Have them cut out of magazines and catalogues three pictures of each type of thing and glue them on their paper in the appropriate category.

Lesson 5

Tell students that there are permanent and temporary magnets. Review with students the properties of magnets. Ask them if they have ever seen something besides a magnet pick up an object in a magnetic way. Brainstorm a list of ways to make objects magnetic.

Presenting the Lessons *(cont.)*

Divide the students into small groups. Gather a large nail, a bar magnet, iron filings, and small paper clips for each group. Reproduce for each student a Neighborly Nail Data Sheet on page 120. Lead students through the following procedure, first using paper clips and then iron filings as the magnetic object:

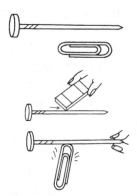

1. With the nail, try to pick up some paper clips. On your data sheet, record what you saw. (Elicit from students that the nail is nonmagnetized.)

2. Now, stroke the nail 25 times in the same direction with one end of the bar magnet.

3. Try again to pick up the paper clips. On your data sheet, record what you saw. (Elicit from students that the nail is now magnetized.)

4. Drop the nail on the floor and then try again to pick up the paper clips. On your data sheet, record what you saw. (Elicit from students that the nail is now demagnetized.)

Curriculum Connections

Art: Tell students they will make a permanent magnet that is also useful. Tell them they will make a crocodile magnet. For each student gather a wooden clothespin, small green pom-pon balls, and small wiggly eyes. Also have on hand white glue and a roll of magnetic tape. Allow students to paint their clothespins green and let them dry before you continue. Cut a piece of magnetic tape for each child, just enough to cover the bottom of the clothespin. Have students glue the pom-pons next to each other on the top side of the clothespin. Have them glue a wiggly eye on each pom-pon. They now have a refrigerator magnet that can hold paper in its "mouth."

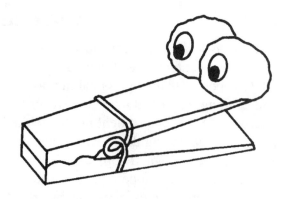

Physical Education: Have students turn themselves into temporary magnets and play magnetic tag. One person is the magnet, while everyone else tries to keep away. As the magnet tags other people, they also become magnetized and have to join the magnet by holding hands. Now the two magnets act as one as they try to tag other students. As more and more students are tagged, they also have to hold on. When the group becomes too large, "demagnetize" everyone (allowing them to drop hands) and designate a new magnet to start again. This is best played in a large open area with marked boundaries.

Math: Have students play Picking up Math Facts. Reproduce and cut out five magnet and 25 nail patterns using page 121. Write one number (4, 5, 6, 7, 8) on each magnet. On each nail, write an addition and/or subtraction equation whose answer is one of the numbers on the magnets. (Make five equation nails for each magnet answer.) Small groups of students can solve the equations on the nails and find which magnet would pick them up. Have students move the nails to be picked up by the poles of the correct magnet.

Make a Little Book

Magnets

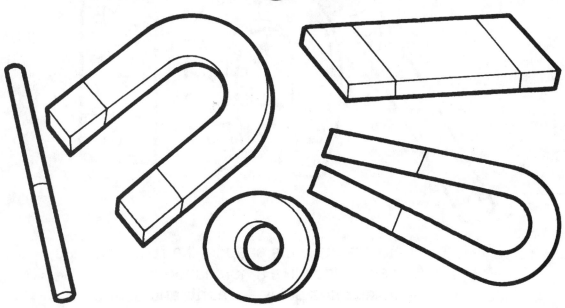

Name _____

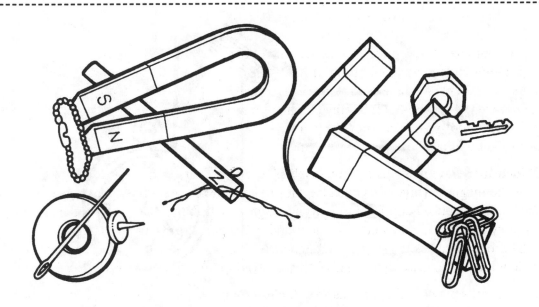

All magnets are attractive,
In whatever shape and size.
They pull some objects toward them
With their ends and all their sides.

1

Make a Little Book *(cont.)*

There are magnets shaped like rods and bars,
And some look like a horseshoe.
Each kind has poles—a north and south.
The south is red; the north is blue.

2

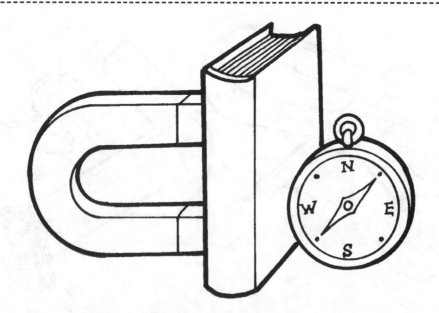

Magnets work through lots of things
Such as water, sand, and air.
They can move a compass through a book
As though it were not there!

3

Make a Little Book *(cont.)*

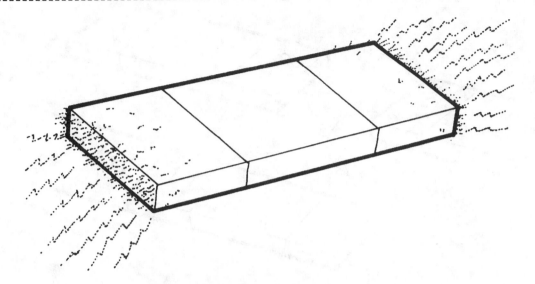

A magnet has magnetic force
And a strong magnetic field.
But its force can also be shut down
With a nonmagnetic shield.

4

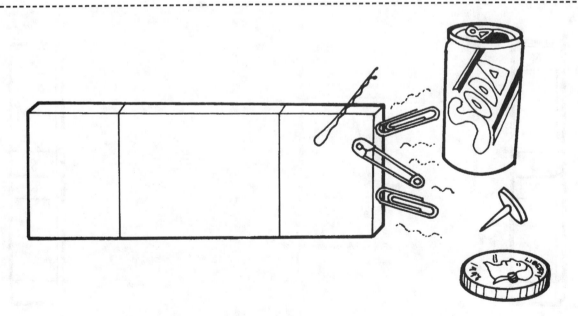

Magnets pull things made of iron,
But it's sometimes hard to tell
Which things a magnet will attract
And which it will repel.

5

Make a Little Book *(cont.)*

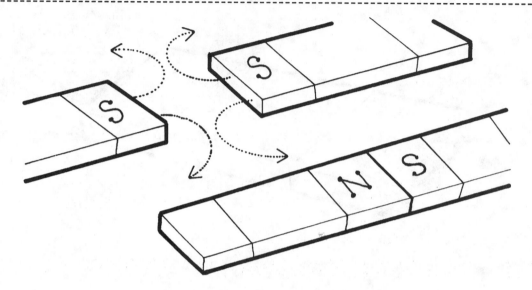

Magnets push away—repel—
Or pull toward—attract.
And though they seem like magic,
They're a scientific fact.

6

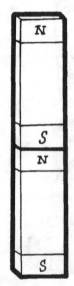

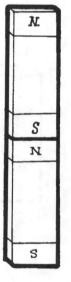

Here is a picture of a magnet attracting something.

7

Just the Facts

Observe a magnet. Do you see anything around it? Put your hand next to the magnet. Do you feel anything? Even though you cannot see or feel it, there is a force there. The force is called magnetism.

Ancient people knew about magnetism. They discovered that a certain kind of rock had a force that made some metal objects stick to it. They also learned that if this rock were hung on a string and allowed to dangle freely, it would always point north and south. This was handy because people needed to know which direction they were traveling, and now they had a stone that could lead them. They called the stone "lead stone," which in English became *lodestone*. Using a lodestone to show north and south became the first compass.

Really, lodestone is not a stone at all, but a piece of iron. Lodestone is a natural magnet. As scientists worked more with magnets, they learned that a magnet has two ends, or poles. A man named William Gilbert studied magnets so much that he finally discovered that the Earth itself is a magnet. It, too, has two poles. We call them the North Pole and the South Pole.

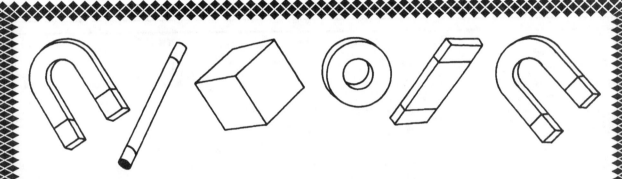

- All magnets have a north pole and a south pole, or opposite magnetic poles.
- Unlike poles (N/S) attract, or pull toward; like poles (N/N and S/S) repel, or push away.
- If you cut a magnet in half, you get a new magnet. Each new magnet will have a north pole and a south pole.
- Objects attracted by a magnet contain iron or steel.
- Magnets can turn ordinary iron and steel objects into magnets themselves. This is called magnetizing.
- Every magnet has an invisible force field around it. The force of the magnet is strongest closest to the magnet.
- An object must come within the magnetic field for the magnet to affect the object by attracting it or repelling it.
- Magnets have different shapes and different magnetic forces.
- The magnetic poles are the strongest parts of a magnet.

Poles Apart

1. Draw a picture and write a sentence about what happened when two north poles were put near each other.

_____

_____

2. Draw a picture and write a sentence about what happened when two south poles were put near each other.

_____

_____

3. Draw a picture and write a sentence about what happened when a north and a south pole were put near each other.

_____

_____

Like or Unlike

Use blue for north poles and red for south poles.

Color the poles so the magnets attract.

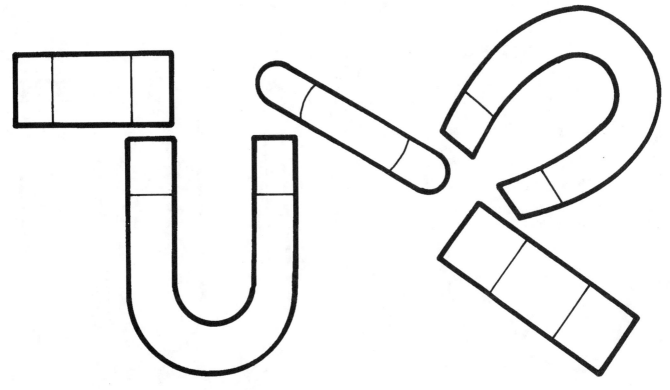

Color the poles so the magnets repel.

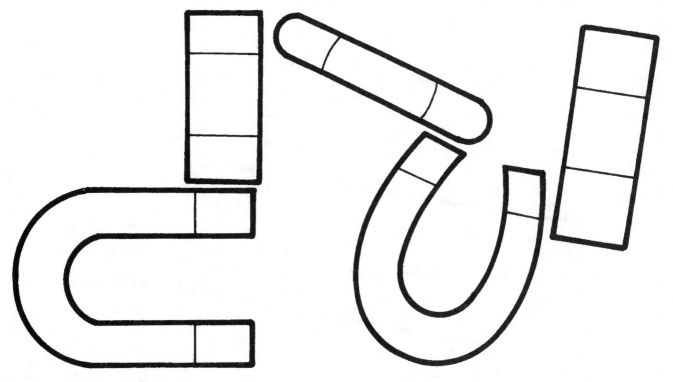

Magnet Patterns

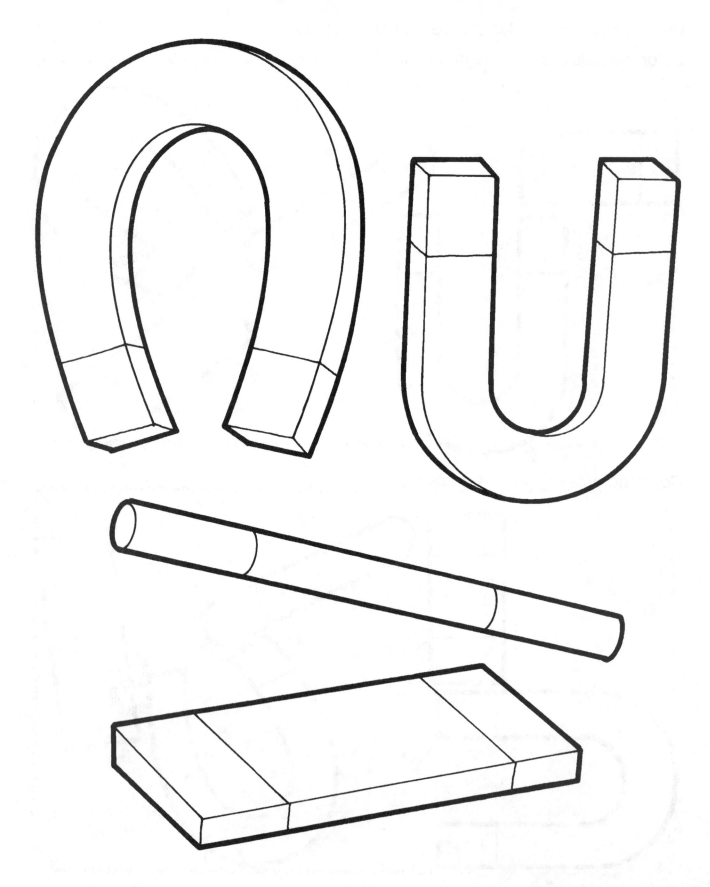

Magnet Hunt

Find two magnets in your house. Draw a picture of where you found each magnet inside a bar magnet below. Complete each sentence.

I found a magnet on _____.

It helps us _____.

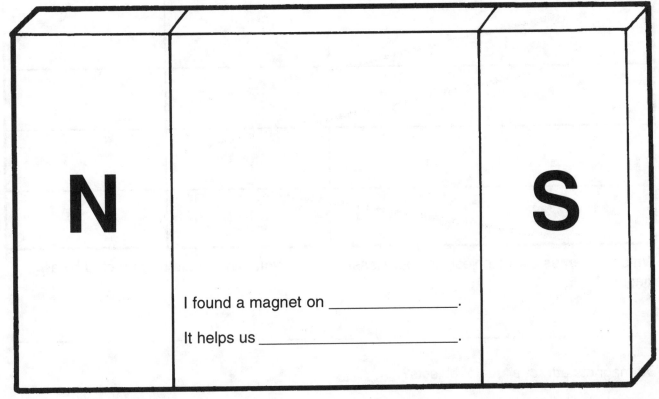

I found a magnet on _____.

It helps us _____.

Attraction Action

Write the name of the object. Put a check mark in the correct place to tell what you saw.

Object	Attracted	Not Attracted

Write the names of five objects in your classroom that you think would be attracted by a magnet.

_____ _____ _____ _____ _____

Do magnets attract all metal objects? _____

Magnetic Muscle

Type of Magnet	Number of Nails Held	Number of Paper Clips Held

List the magnets from strongest to weakest.

Strongest 1._____

2._____

3._____

4._____

5._____

Weakest 6._____

Which magnet seemed to be the strongest? _____

_____

_____

Which objects were the magnets able to pick up more of? Why do you think this happened?

_____

_____

_____

Garage Pattern

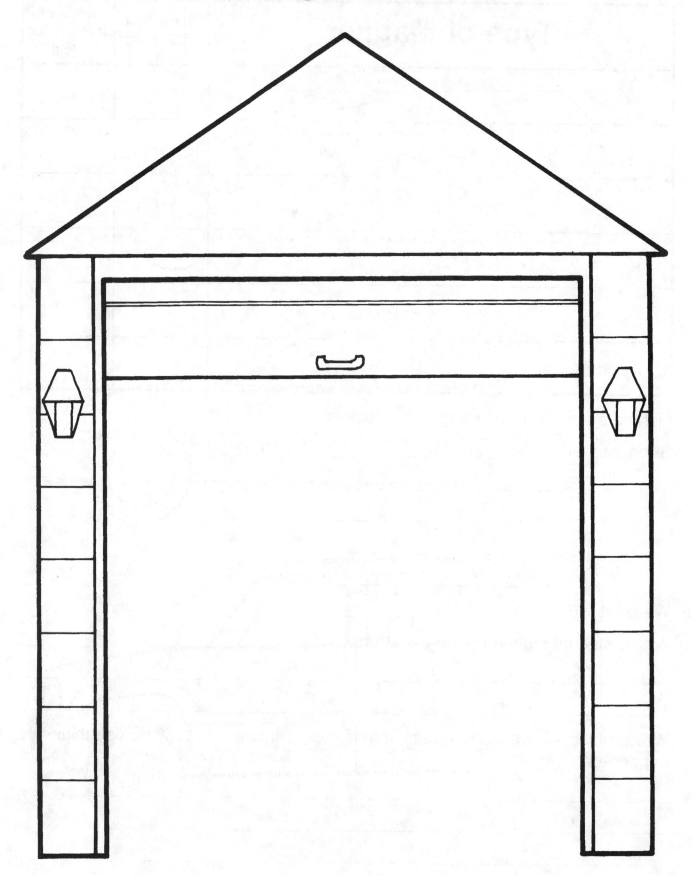

Car Patterns

Magnetic Field Map

What is a magnetic field?

Where around the bar magnet is the magnetic field the strongest?

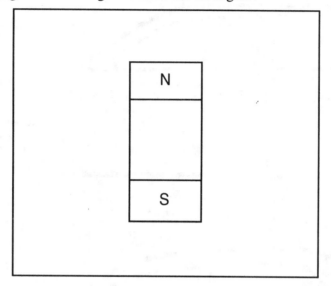

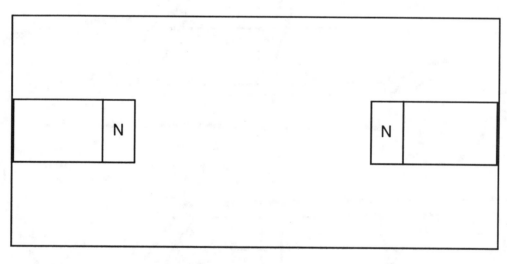

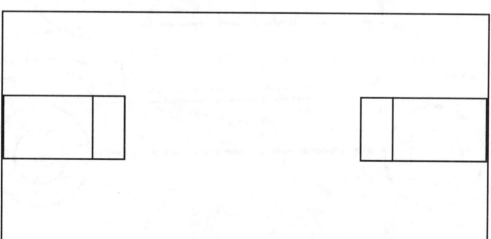

Iron Man

Buried Treasure

Check off all the treasure items you find.

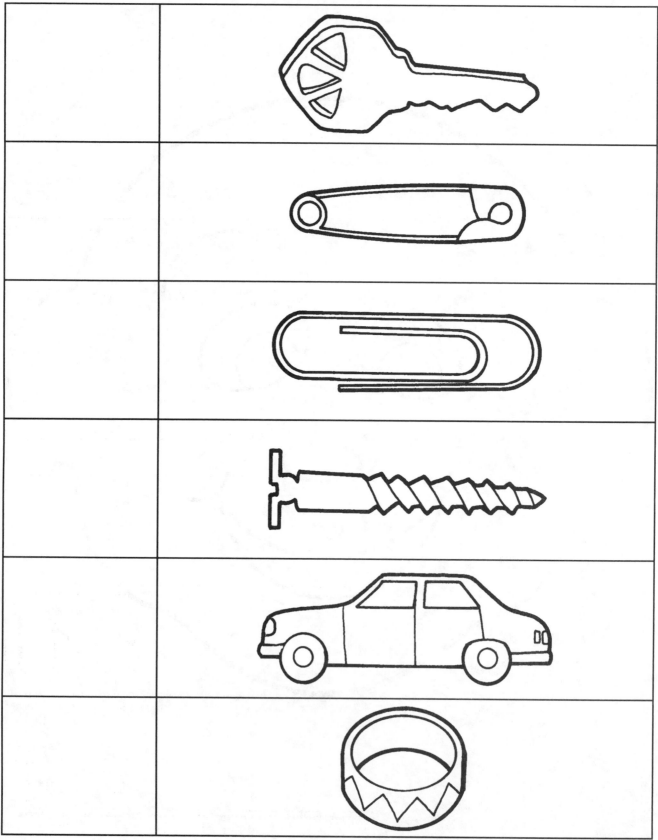

Magnetic Shield Observation Chart

Material	Layers	Distance

Example

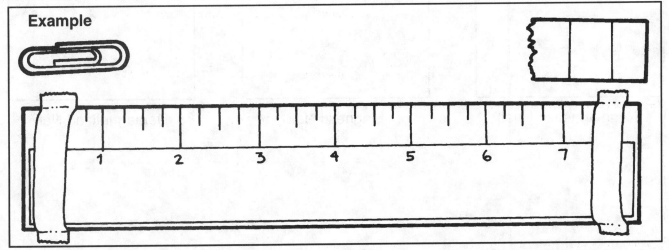

Neighborly Nail Data Sheet

In the boxes, draw what you observed.

Picking up a paper clip with a nail.

Nonmagnetized Nail   Magnetic Nail   Demagnetized Nail

Picking up iron filings with a nail

Nonmagnetized Nail   Magnetic Nail   Demagnetized Nail

Picking Up Math Facts Patterns

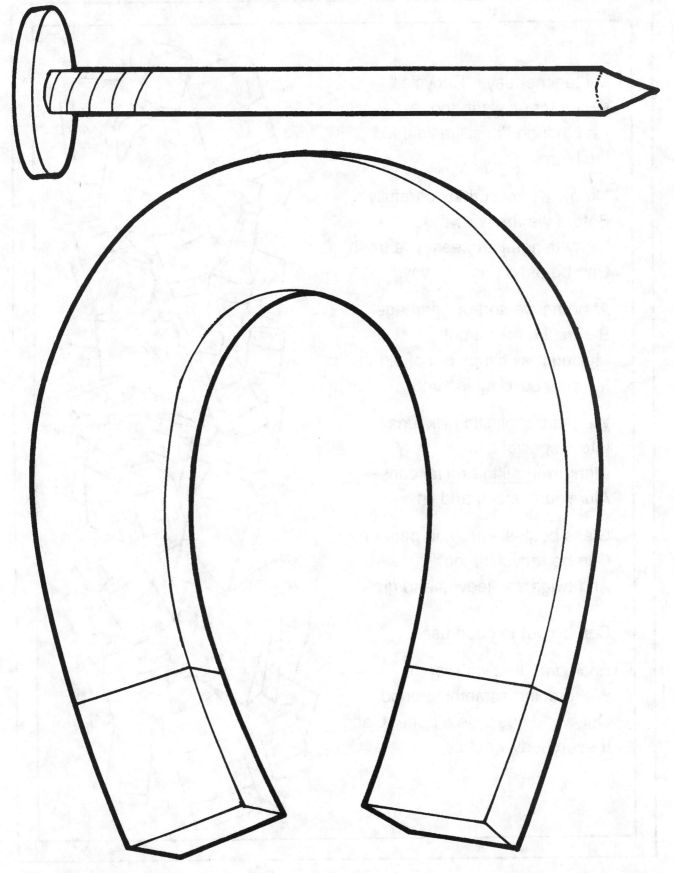

Recycling

My teacher says "Recycle."
My mother says it, too.
And though I'm still a little kid,
I'm learning what to do.

I know we must think carefully
Before we throw away.
Many things that seem like trash
Can be used another way.

At home we sort our garbage
Before we take it out.
Making new things out of old things
Is what recycling is about.

We put our plastic milk jugs
Into a special bin.
Along with all the metal cans—
Aluminum, steel, and tin.

Glass bottles, jars, and paper bags
Can be recycled, too.
And twigs and leaves and grass
  clippings
Can be put to good use.

Each time that we recycle,
We're doing something good.
Our world could be a better place
If everybody would.

122

Recycling

Presenting the Lessons

Objectives: Students will learn what recycling is, what can be recycled, how to recycle correctly, the reasons for recycling, and their role in making our world a better, cleaner place through recycling.

Unit Poem and Little Book: "Recycling"

Lesson 1

Read aloud the poem "Recycling" on page 122. Discuss with the class the meaning of the word recycle, and encourage students to share ideas and experiences they have had with recycling at home and at school.

Tell students what they will learn about recycling. Have students assemble and color the Little Books (pages 127–130). Make a class Big Book from the Little Book (see suggestions on page 2). Display and read aloud the Big Book as students read along in their Little Books. Elicit from students the kinds of things the poem says to recycle (plastic, cans, paper, yard waste, glass).

Reproduce I'm a Recycling Kid badges (page 131) for students to wear each day of the unit. Tell students that the symbol on the badge is found on many materials that are recyclable or have been recycled.

Present the Taking Out the Trash activity on page 132.

Reproduce and send home the Parent Letter on page 133.

Curriculum Connections

Art: Begin a recycling bulletin board. Enlarge five recycling bin patterns (page 131). Attach the bins to the bulletin board and label them Cans, Paper, Plastic, Glass, and Yard Waste. Have students cut out pictures of these kinds of recyclable items from magazines and catalogues and place them in the proper bins.

Math: Have students count the number of items in each of the boxes and the garbage can in the Taking Out the Trash activity (page 132.) On the chalkboard, make a bar graph showing the results of their recycling efforts on "Trash Day."

Presenting the Lessons *(cont.)*

Phonics: Sing a recycling song to the tune of "Here We Go Looby Loo." For each verse, substitute a different item that can be recycled.

Recycle begins with R.

Recycle begins with R.

We'll recycle newspapers. (glass, aluminum, yard waste, etc.)

Recycle begins with R.

Lesson 2

Read aloud the Big Book as students read along in their Little Books. Have them listen for the part of the poem that tells why we should recycle (verses 2 and 3—things can be used another way, making new things out of old things). Tell students that they are going to learn what happens to our garbage after it leaves our houses.

Have a speaker from the city sanitation department visit the class to explain what happens to garbage after it is collected. Make sure the speaker covers such things as the problems associated with garbage dumps and landfills (nonbiodegradable items, toxic substances, etc.) and the importance of recycling. If a speaker is not available, check with your school district's media center for movies, videos, kits, or other teaching aids.

Tell students they will do an experiment that will help them better understand the importance of recycling. Present the Down in the Dumps activity on page 134.

Curriculum Connections

Math: Gather a large assortment of small, hard items such as buttons, nuts, bolts, screws, and bottle caps. Give each student a small paper cup full of these items. Toss a standard die. Select one student to count the dots, and have the other students form that numeral using their items.

Phonics: Make a word web bulletin board. On a construction paper oval, write "R Is for . . . " and attach it to the center of the bulletin board. On another paper write "Recycle." Attach it to the bulletin board, and connect it to the large oval using a piece of string. Cut out and laminate pictures of things that begin with *r* and some that don't. Place the pictures into a paper bag, and have students take turns pulling out a picture. Have the student say the name of the picture and decide whether it starts with the same sound as in "recycle" *(r)*. If it does, have the student add the picture to the word web. If it doesn't, have the student draw a picture of something that does begin with *r* and add it to the word web.

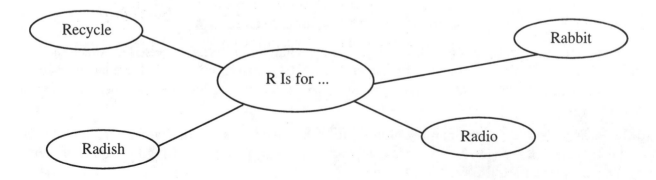

Presenting the Lessons *(cont.)*

Lesson 3

Read aloud the Big Book as students read along in their Little Books. Elicit from them the sequence for recycling: think before throwing away, sort, recycle. Elicit from students why sorting is necessary, and discuss ways that things could be used in another way rather than discarded as trash.

Take the class on a field trip to a recycling center or have a speaker from a center come and tell the class what is done with the different types of discarded but recyclable items.

Write a class letter to city officials either commending the city on having a recycling program or encouraging them to start one.

Make recycled paper. Tell students they are going to recycle old newspaper into "new paper." Present the Newspaper Becomes New Paper activity on page 135.

Curriculum Connections

Math: Prepare a Recycling Center Game Board (page 136). Make a die from a wooden or sponge cube, and write the numbers 0–5 on its sides. Obtain four small toy trucks. Let groups of four students play at a time. Students take turns rolling the die. Each student reads the number he or she rolled and moves his or her truck that many spaces on the board. If the student rolls a zero, it means he or she forgot to recycle and must go back to start. The first person to the recycling center wins.

Physical Education: Lead students in a game of "Mother, May I Recycle?" Have them line up on a starting line. Stand at the finish line, and call on individuals to take a number of baby, medium, or giant steps when you tell them to recycle an item. (Example: "John, you may take two baby steps to recycle a plastic milk jug.") The student must say "Mother, may I recycle?" before moving. If the child forgets, he or she must go back to the starting line.

Phonics: Reproduce a Recycle Begins with "R" (page 137) for each student. Have students cut out the pictures and glue the ones that begin with the *r* sound onto the recycling bin.

Lesson 4

Explain to students that we can recycle many things even before they ever get to a recycling center. Remind students that the poem in their Little Books says that many things can be put to good use. Elicit from students ways that things can be reused or made into something new. Examples are turning old cans into pencil holders, cutting off jeans into shorts, or even handing down or trading clothes with smaller kids or friends.

Presenting the Lessons *(cont.)*

Tell students that they will be turning the classroom into a recycling center, and they will help you recycle things that seem like trash. Present one or more of the activities on pages 138–143.

Curriculum Connections

Math: Play Bottle Bowling. Gather 20 empty, plastic two-liter bottles and two volleyballs. Using 10 bottles for each, form two triangles by placing the bottles about four inches apart. Divide the class into two teams, and name each team. Write the team names on the chalkboard. Line teams up 10–12 feet from the "bowling pins." Give each team a ball and let each student have a turn bowling. After their turn, students will count the number of bottles knocked down and record that number under their team's column on the chalkboard. When all students have bowled, add the columns to determine the winning team.

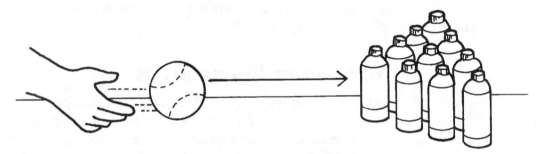

Music: Form a rhythm band using items that would be discarded. Drums and rhythm sticks: boxes, cans, and wood scraps; Horns: paper tubes; Maracas: jars or bottles filled with buttons, rice, or beans; etc. Play a simple song, and have the "band" play and sing along.

Lesson 5

As a culminating activity, take students to the playground or a nearby park and have a clean-up day. Provide garbage bags and disposable plastic gloves for collecting the trash. Adults should supervise small groups of students carefully so they do not pick up anything harmful. When they come back together, have students sort the trash into the five main categories you have studied: metal, glass, plastic, paper, and yard waste. See which pile is bigger. Take pictures of the clean-up activities and display them in the hallway or send them to the local newspaper with a letter about recycling. Make sure to have childern clean-up their hands and to wash with anti-bacterial soap when they are through.

Have a Recycling Party. Have students make woven placemats (page 140). Then serve cookies on paper plates, drinks in paper cups, and use napkins made from recycled paper.

Make a Little Book

Recycling

Name _____

My teacher says "Recycle."
My mother says it, too.
And though I'm still a little kid,
I'm learning what to do.

1

Make a Little Book *(cont.)*

I know we must think carefully
Before we throw away.
Many things that seem like trash
Can be used another way.

2

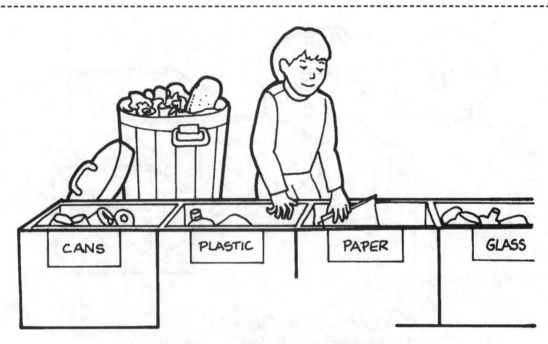

At home we sort our garbage
Before we take it out.
Making new things out of old things
Is what recycling is about.

3

Make a Little Book *(cont.)*

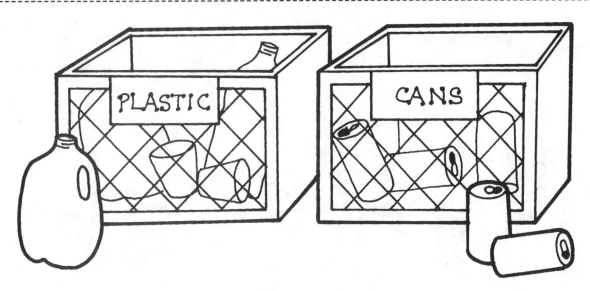

We put our plastic milk jugs
Into a special bin;
Along with all the metal cans—
Aluminum, steel, and tin.

4

Glass bottles, jars, and paper bags
Can be recycled, too.
And twigs and leaves and grass clippings
Can be put to good use.

5

Make a Little Book *(cont.)*

Each time that we recycle,
We're doing something good.
Our world could be a better place
If everybody would.

6

This is what I recycle.

7

Patterns

I'm a
Recycling
Kid

Recycle

Taking Out the Trash

Materials:

- Five boxes labeled Plastic, Paper, Metal, Glass, and Yard Waste
- Several recyclable and nonrecyclable items for each category

- Garbage can
- Large trash bag
- Crayons
- Drawing paper

Preparing for the Activity:

Put all trash items in the trash bag. Place the labeled boxes and the garbage can at the front of the classroom. Distribute drawing paper to students.

Teaching the Activity:

1. Tell students that today is trash day and they are going to help you take out the trash by sorting it for recycling.
2. Dump the trash out of the bag onto the floor.
3. Discuss the difference between things that are recyclable and things that are not.
4. Have a volunteer select an item and tell where it belongs—in a recycle box or the garbage can.
5. Have the volunteer place the item in the appropriate place.
6. Continue until all items have been placed.
7. Encourage students to think of additional recyclable and nonrecyclable trash items, draw a picture of each one, and place the picture in the appropriate place.

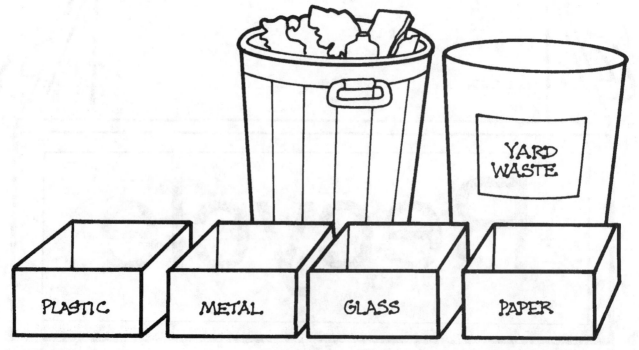

Parent Letter

Dear Parent,

Our new science theme unit is "Recycling." During this unit, we will be learning more about what recycling is, what kinds of things can be recycled, and the advantages of recycling. Activities will extend across the curriculum to include math, art, physical education, music, and phonics.

As part of this unit, your child will be bringing home a Little Book about recycling. Read it aloud with your child and ask your child to tell you what he or she thinks about recycling. Encourage your child to "teach" you about recycling. To reinforce learning, ask your child what he or she has learned each day.

Here are some activities we do!

1. Sorting trash into recyclables and nonrecyclables
2. An experiment that shows how things do and do not degrade in a landfill
3. Making recycled paper from old newspaper
4. Using trash to make creative treasures

If possible, help your child collect and bring to class such things as empty, clean milk jugs and metal cans; plastic six-pack rings; and assorted objects such as buttons, nuts, bolts, or other junk items.

As a culminating activity, we will be having a clean-up day at a park or playground. If you would like to be notified when that is and can help supervise the activity, please complete and return the form below.

Thank you for your support of your child and our class!

Sincerely, _____

- -

I would like to be notified of the date and time of the class clean-up day. I may be able to help supervise the students.

Signed: _____

Evening Phone Number: _____

Down in the Dumps

Objective: Through long-term observation, students will learn and understand the lasting effects of nonbiodegradable items that are put into landfills instead of being recycled.

Materials:

- Five 2-liter plastic bottles with the tops cut off
- Garden or yard soil
- Water
- Leaves, weeds, twigs, and grass clippings
- Plastic spoon or fork
- Strips of newspaper
- 2–3 nails
- Small glass jar
- Masking tape
- Marking pen
- Cardboard

Procedures:

1. Fill each plastic bottle half full with soil.

2. With the marking pen, label pieces of masking tape #1 Yard Waste, #2 Plastic, #3 Paper, #4 Metal, #5 Glass, and attach a label to each bottle.

3. Put the items into the appropriate bottle and cover them completely with soil.

4. Use just enough water in each bottle to moisten the soil.

5. Close the tops of the bottles by taping a cardboard circle on as a lid.

Discussion: Elicit from students predictions about what will happen in each bottle and why.

Observations: Make an observation chart and record the condition of the items in each bottle at the beginning of the experiment. Every few days, check the contents and record any changes.

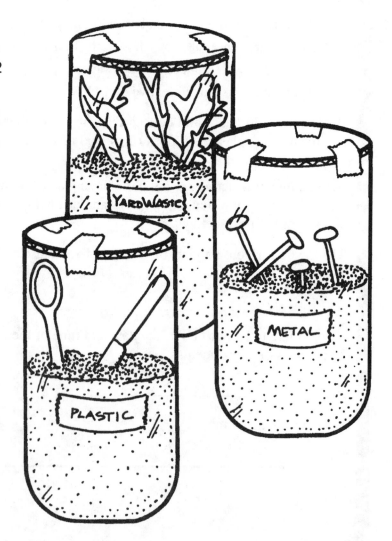

Newspaper Becomes New Paper

Materials:

- Newspaper
- Water
- Wire whisk
- Bucket
- Cornstarch

- ¼ cup (63 mL) measuring cup
- Window screening
- Wooden spoon
- Rolling pin

Directions:

1. Fill the bucket half full of newspaper torn into small pieces.
2. Add water to a level about 2 inches (5 cm) above the paper.
3. Let the paper soak overnight.
4. Add ¼ cup (63 mL) of cornstarch to the paper/water mixture.
5. Beat the mixture with a whisk until it becomes a pulp.
6. Scoop some pulp onto the window screening.
7. Hold the screening over the bucket to catch drips as you spread the pulp to about ⅛" (.3 cm) thickness with the wooden spoon.
8. Place the screen and wet pulp between thicknesses of newspaper to blot the excess water as you roll over it with the rolling pin.
9. Remove the blotting paper.
10. Allow to dry overnight, then gently peel the recycled paper from the screen.

Recycling Center Game Board

Recycle Begins with "R"

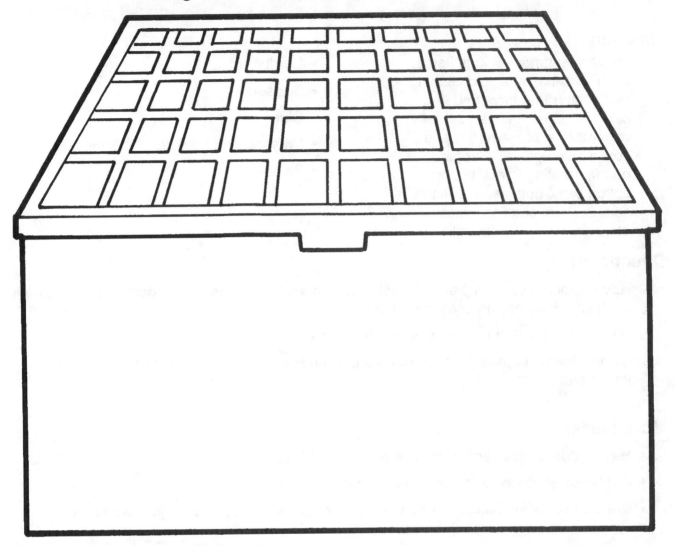

Trashy Treasures

Materials:

- Large assortment of junk items, such as cans, cups, old clothing, jars, foam meat trays and egg cartons, paper towel and toilet paper tubes, old jewelry, used construction paper, wrapping paper, greeting cards, ribbon, cotton balls, buttons, material scraps, yarn, sequins, glitter, etc.

- Cardboard
- Scissors
- Glue
- Crayons and markers
- Paint

Directions:

1. Have students select a piece of trash and turn it into a "treasure" by decorating it, using it in a picture, or making something new with it.

2. Have them share their creations with the class.

3. Display them in a hallway case or on a bulletin board so other classes can see how things can be recycled.

More Ideas:

- Have students use cardboard as a base for a junk sculpture.
- Challenge students to create something useful from junk.
- Paint and/or color the cardboard base, the trashy treasure, and the junk sculpture.

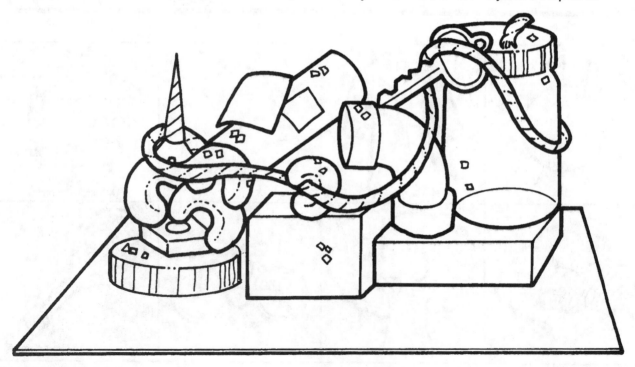

Milk Jug Creations

Materials:

- 1-gallon (3.8 L) plastic milk jug
- Tempera paints
- Paintbrush
- Dishwashing soap
- Scissors

Directions:

1. Cut the handle and the spout off the jug.
2. Trim the jug into a helmet shape to fit your head.
3. Add a few drops of dishwashing soap to the paint and paint your helmet.

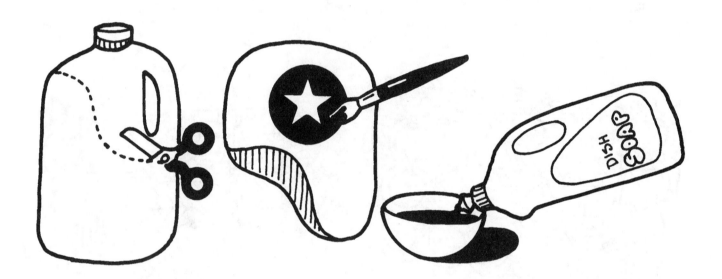

More Ideas:

- Paint the helmet gray and add a topknot of red construction paper feathers to make a knight's helmet.

- Make elephant bookends by painting the milk jugs to look like elephants, gluing on paper or felt eyes and ears, and half-filling the jugs with uncooked rice or sand.

- Create different milk-jug animals.

                                   #0044 Science Explorations

Six-Pack-Ring Weaving

Materials:

- 4 plastic six-pack rings
- Twist ties
- Yarn, string, and ribbon
- Strips of paper or fabric
- Glue
- Scissors

Directions:

1. Attach the rings together with twist ties to form a large rectangle.
2. Weave yarn, string, ribbon, and paper or fabric strips through the holes.
3. Trim the excess weaving materials around the edges and glue or staple the ends to the plastic rings.

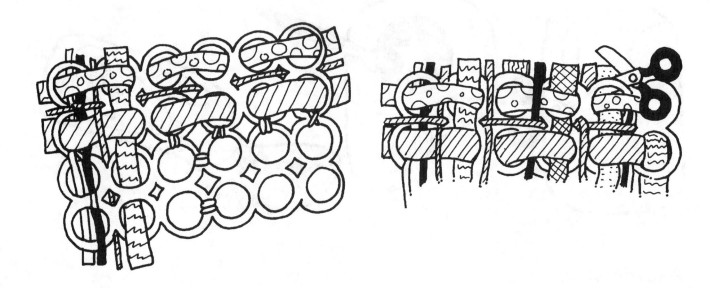

More Ideas:

- Weave in items collected from nature.
- Weave a set of placemats.
- Make a large weaving for a wall-hanging, using more rings.

Canned Goods

Materials:

- Metal can, clean and empty
- Soda can, clean and empty
- Acrylic paints
- Paintbrush
- Pipe cleaners
- Paper or felt

Metal Can Holders

Directions:

1. Paint the outside of the metal can a solid color and let it dry.
2. Paint a scene or design on the can.

More Ideas:

- Use the can for a votive candle.
- Use the can for a pencil holder.
- Use the can as a vase for real or artificial flowers.
- Glue glitter, sequins, or items found in nature to the can.

Soda Can Critters

Directions:

1. Crush the can by stomping on it.
2. Using the drink hole as the mouth, add facial features of paint, pipe cleaners, paper, or felt.

More Ideas:

- Create a class mobile by punching a hole in the critters and hanging them with string from coat hangers.
- Have the class create a Crushed Critter zoo.

Newspaper Fan

Materials:

- Newspaper, cut into rectangle
- Scissors
- Yarn or ribbon
- Hole punch
- Watercolor paints
- Paintbrush
- Stapler or tape

Directions:

1. Watercolor paint both sides of the newspaper, making several bands of color. Let dry.

2. Accordion pleat the sheet of newspaper and tape or staple one end.

3. Make a bow out of yarn or ribbon and attach it to the fastened end.

4. Punch holes along the top edge of the fan and weave ribbon through the holes. Tape or staple the end pieces to the fan.

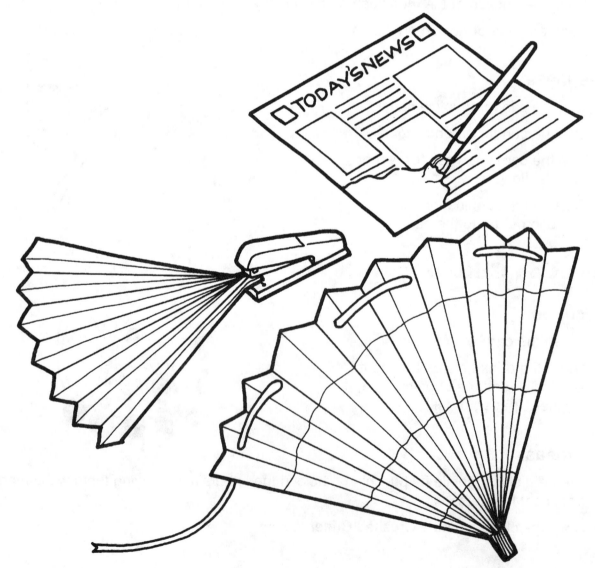

Pocket Pouch

Materials:

- Pair of old pants with back pocket attached
- 25" (63.5 cm) piece of ribbon, yarn, string, or twine
- Stapler
- Scissors
- Glue
- Sequins, glitter, buttons, and other small items for decorating

Directions:

1. Make a pouch by cutting a back pocket out of (not off of) the pants, leaving the pant material behind the pocket.
2. Staple a strap to the sides of the pouch.
3. Decorate the pouch.

More Ideas:

- Cut two slits in the back of the pouch to slide onto a belt.
- Cut slits all the way around the top of the pouch about one inch apart. Weave ribbon, yarn, string, or twine through the slits to create a drawstring bag.

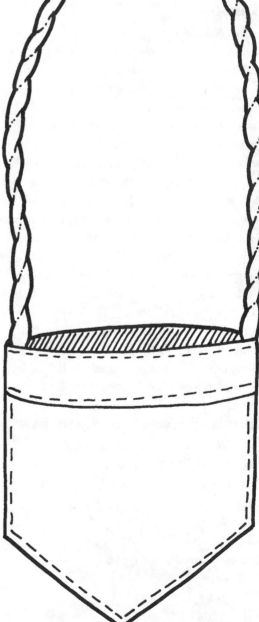

Bibliography and Resources

Technology

The Backyard. Lab Pack (5 program disks). Broderbund. P.O. Box 6125, Novato, CA 94948. 1–800–474–8840. Creative activity program helps develop readiness skills; keyboard overlay for children with special needs. (PreK–3)

Magnetism: Why Does a Compass Point North? Let's Explore Magnets. Video. ATI The Learning Source. 1–800–457–4509.

Seasons. CD-ROM for Mac or MPC; Lab Pack (5 program disks). National Geographic. 1–800–955–5570. Students experience the changes that occur in all four seasons. (K–3)

Seed Scientist and Plant Growth. Software. K–5 Math and Science Software, HyperTech Media, Inc.

What's Inside a Seed? Laserdisc CAV. Wonder World of Science, Coronet/MTI. 1–800–955–5570. Students learn about seed plants—how they grow, what they need to grow, and how flowers produce more seeds. (K–3)

Wooly's Garden. Lab Pack (5 program disks). MECC. Simulation program teaches science inquiry skills through the discovery of how the needs of plants influence their growth. (K–2)

World of Plants. CD-ROM for Mac or MPC; Lab Pack (5 program disks). National Geographic. 1–800–955–5570. Students read along as they learn about the life of plants and how the seasons affect them. (K–3; ESL)

Books

Ardley, Neil. *Science Book of Magnets.* HBJ, 1991.

Back, Christine. *Spider's Web.* Silver Burdett Co., 1986.

Barklem, Jill. *Autumn Story, Spring Story, Summer Story, Winter Story.* Putnam, 1986.

Berger, Melvin. *Seasons.* Doubleday, 1990.

Brandt, Keith. *Wonders of the Seasons.* Troll, 1982.

Carle, Eric. *The Tiny Seed.* Picture Book, 1991.

Challand, Helen. *Experiments with Magnets.* Childrens Press, 1986.

Davies, Kay and Wendy Oldfield. *Electricity and Magnetism.* Starting Science Series, Steck-Vaughan Company, 1992.

Dorros, Arthur. *Me and My Shadow.* Scholastic, 1990.

Florian, Douglas. *Vegetable Garden.* Harcourt, 1991.

Fowler, Allan. *What's Your Favorite Flower?* Rookie Read-About-Science series, Childrens, 1992.

Hiscock, Bruce. *The Big Tree.* Macmillan, 1991.

King, Elizabeth. *Backyard Sunflower.* Dutton, 1993.

Kirkpatrick, Rena K. *Look at Leaves.* Raintree, 1985.

Krull, Kathleen. *It's My Earth, Too: How I Can Help the Earth Stay Alive.* Doubleday, 1992.

Lane, Margaret. *The Spider.* The Dial Press, 1982.

Pearson, Susan. *My Favorite Time of Year.* Harper, 1988.

Santrey, Laurence. *Magnets.* Troll Assocs., 1988.

Souza, D.M. *Eight Legs.* Carolrhoda Books, Inc., 1991.

Wexler, Jerome. *Flowers, Fruits, and Seeds.* Simon & Schuster, 1991.

Teacher Created Materials

#201 *Whole Language Units for Science*

#286 Thematic Unit—*Ecology*

#591 Thematic Unit—*Spiders*

Hands-On Minds-On Science series

#625 *Plants*

#633 *Ecology*

#643 *Magnetism and Electricity*

#612 *Magnets*

#676 *Art for All Seasons*

#678 *Creative Crafts for Clever Kids*